365
Stories
and
Rhymes
for
GIRLS

PRODUCED FOR CHAD VALLEY TOYS
489-499 Avebury Boulevard,
Central Milton Keynes, MK9 2NW

www.argos.co.uk

ISBN 978-1-4723-1091-0
Batch Code: S37620
Made in China

365

Stories
and
Rhymes
for

GIRLS

Contents

The Frog Prince

Once upon a time there lived a princess who shone with such beauty that even the sun looked dim next to her.

When the weather was hot, the princess would walk through the forest and sit in the shade by a stream. She took a golden ball to play with, and sat by the water, throwing it into the air and catching it. But one day, her hand slipped and the golden ball fell into the water with a splash!

The princess sat there and cried, louder and louder until it sounded as if her heart would break. After a while, a warty frog popped his head above the water.

"Why are you crying so?" he asked.

"Because I have dropped my golden ball into the stream and I can't get it back," sobbed the princess.

"What will you give me if I fetch your ball?" croaked the frog.

"I will give you jewels, gold and pearls. If you bring back my golden ball, I will give you anything you want," sniffed the princess through her tears.

But the frog explained that he wasn't interested in treasures. Instead, he wanted the princess's love.

"If you will love me and care for me, be my friend and play with me, let me eat from your plate and sleep on your pillow, then I will fetch back your ball," said the frog.

"Yes. I promise that I will do all of those things," said the princess. But really, she didn't mean what she said.

"He is just a revolting frog," she thought. "He will give back my ball and then I won't do any of those things."

The frog brought back the princess's ball. She took it from him and then ran back to the palace.

That evening, as the royal family sat down to eat, there was a knock at the door. The princess went to see who was there and was horrified to find the frog, who spoke these words:

"Let me in, oh princess sweet,
Don't forget your vow.
Let me be your own dear love.
To your heart, I bow."

But the princess slammed the door in the frog's face and hurried back to the table.

"Who was that?" asked her father.

"Oh, just a slimy frog," replied the princess. "He would only fetch my ball back for me if I promised to love him. How ridiculous, to think that I should love a warty old frog!"

"A promise is a promise," said the king, who was a fair man. "You must let him in and keep your promise."

And so, much to the princess's dismay, the frog was invited in. The king commanded his daughter to keep her promise and, although she found the frog quite disgusting, she had no choice but to obey her father. The princess allowed the frog to eat from her plate and sleep on her pillow, she even played games with him. But she could not bring herself to care for him or love him. The frog reminded her of the promise she had made to him, saying these words:

"Love me true, oh princess sweet,
Don't forget your vow.
Let me be your own dear love,
You must kiss me now."

But still the princess refused to kiss him.
The frog followed the princess everywhere she went until she became quite angry with him.

"Go away, you horrible beast!" she cried, but the frog stayed by her side night and day.

One day, when the princess was in a particularly bad mood, she picked up the frog and hurled him across the room. He hit the wall and landed on the floor with a bump! He lay there, dazed, and had such a sad expression on his face that the princess felt sorry for what she had done. She rushed over to where he lay, picked him up and kissed him with true compassion.

Suddenly, there was a flash of light and the astonished princess watched on as the frog was transformed into a handsome prince.

"My dear princess," said the prince, falling to his knees. "Please be my wife."

The princess knew for sure that she loved the prince, and that finally her promise was fulfilled. The prince and princess were married in a spectacular ceremony and the bride shone more brightly than the sun. They lived happily ever after.

Seven Ravens

Once there lived a man and a woman who had seven sons, but longed for a daughter. When their eighth child was a girl, they were very happy. At last their wish had come true.

The beautiful baby girl was a thirsty little thing, so the seven sons were sent out to the well to fetch water.

"Take this silver cup and fill it for the baby," said their mother. But the silver cup fell into the well with a splash! The boys were too frightened to go home.

When they didn't return, their father cursed them. "May those lazy good-for-nothing boys become ravens!" he shouted. As soon as the words left his mouth, he saw seven ravens flying off into the distance. Although he regretted his words, it was too late to undo his curse.

When the little girl grew older, her sad mother told her all about her seven lost brothers. The brave girl vowed to find them and bring them home.

She set off, taking her mother's ring as a keepsake, and searched the world over. "Where are my seven brothers?" she called up to the heavens. The stars could see that the poor girl was in despair and took

pity on her. They sent down a magical key and, as the girl picked it up, she heard these words:

"Follow our light to a mountain of glass,
You'll find your raven brothers at last."

After walking for many days, the young girl finally reached the glass mountain. Using the key she entered a crystal cave and, although nobody was there, she noticed seven little plates and cups laid out with food and drink ready for their return.

Being very hungry, she took a bite from each plate and a sip from each cup. Her ring fell into the last cup but, before she could pick it up again, she heard the swish of wings. She hid behind a door and watched seven ravens swoop down.

Each raven noticed that some of their food and drink was missing. Then the last raven found the ring in his cup and recognised it as his mother's.

"If only our little sister has come to find us," he exclaimed, "for then we could return home with her."

On hearing this, their brave little sister jumped out from behind the door. As soon as they saw her, the ravens turned back into their human form.

They returned home to a huge celebration and lived happily ever after.

Jack and Jill

Jack and Jill went up the hill
To fetch a pail of water;
Jack fell down and broke his crown,
And Jill came tumbling after.
Up Jack got, and home did trot
As fast as he could caper;
He went to bed, to mend his head,
With vinegar and brown paper.

Sparrow

Little brown sparrow, sat upon a tree,
Way up in the branches, safe as he can be!
Hopping through the green leaves, he will play,
High above the ground is where he will stay.

Cobbler, Cobbler

Cobbler, cobbler, mend my shoe,
Get it done by half past two.
Half past two is much too late!
Get it done by half past eight.

Little Miss Muffet

Little Miss Muffet
Sat on a tuffet,
Eating her curds and whey;
Along came a spider,
Who sat down beside her
And frightened Miss Muffet away.

See-Saw, Margery Daw

See-saw, Margery Daw,
Johnny shall have a new master;
He shall have but a penny a day,
Because he can't work any faster.

The Grand Old Duke of York

The grand old Duke of York,
He had ten thousand men,
He marched them up to the top of the hill,
And he marched them down again.
When they were up, they were up,
And when they were down, they were down,
And when they were only half way up,
They were neither up nor down.

Elsie Elephant's Jungle Shower

There wasn't a cloud in the sky, and Elsie Elephant was feeling very hot.

"It's even hot in the shade," she grumbled. "I think I'll go to the river to cool off!"

Tommy Monkey was swinging high up in the tree-tops. "I'm going swimming," Elsie told him. "You can come too, if you like."

"You've got a very long trunk," said Tommy as they wandered towards the river. "What's it for?"

Elsie thought for a minute. "I'm not really sure," she said.

At the river they found Leo Lion standing at the edge of the water, looking in.

"Are you coming for a swim?" asked Elsie.

"Big cats don't swim," sighed Leo. "But I'm so hot!" He watched as Elsie and Tommy splashed into the river.

Elsie saw how hot Leo looked. She looked at her trunk – and had an idea! Filling her trunk with water, she sprayed it all over Leo.

"Thanks, Elsie. This is great!" said Leo.

"*Now* I know what my long trunk is for!" laughed Elsie.

Thank You, Kitty

"Kitty," called Cat one day. "I've got a surprise for you."

Kitty bounced over.

"You can have lots of fun with this ball of wool," said Cat.

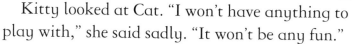

Soon Kitty was leaping around. "Watch me, Mum!" she shouted.

"Kitty," called Mother Bird. "Please may I have some wool for my nest?"

Kitty looked at Cat. "I won't have anything to play with," she said sadly. "It won't be any fun."

Cat smiled. "It's much more fun to share things," she said.

Kitty and Cat watched the bird tuck the wool into her nest.

"The baby birds like the wool, don't they, Mum?" laughed Kitty. "I like sharing. Who else can I share my wool with?"

"Why don't you ask the rabbits?" said Cat.

"We're having a hopping race," said Little Rabbit. "A piece of wool is just what we need to make a finishing line. Thank you!"

Just then Cat called Kitty over. "I have a surprise for you," she said. "It's a bell from Mother Bird. To thank you for sharing your wool."

"What a lovely present," said Kitty. "Would you like to play with it too, Mum?"

Brave Billy Bunny

At the edge of Frog Pond Wood lived a friendly little bunny called Billy and his little brother Bobby.

Now the one thing Billy really, really hated was getting wet! So, one sunny day, when the other bunnies and Bobby hopped off to the stream to play, Billy ran through the wood instead, leaping over logs and weaving in and out of the trees. He was very fast!

Suddenly, he heard someone calling his name. It was Bouncer Bunny. "Billy! Come quickly!" he panted. "Bobby's fallen into the deep water and is being washed away!"

Billy rushed off towards the stream, leaving Bouncer far behind. When he reached it, he could just see Bobby in the distance, being quickly washed away downstream.

"Help!" cried Bobby. "I can't swim!"

Then Billy began to run! He managed to get ahead of Bobby. Then he jumped into the water, swam up to his brother and, coughing and spluttering, dragged Bobby to the side.

"Billy!" cried the others. "You're a hero!"

"A wet hero!" said Billy, grinning. "Getting wet wasn't so bad after all. I'm going for another swim – in the shallows!"

Katy and the Butterfly

As Katy Kitten lay dozing happily in the sun, something tickled her nose. She opened an eye and saw a butterfly fluttering just above her whiskers.

Katy sprang after the butterfly, missed it and landed in a bed of thistles.

"I'll catch that butterfly!" she said, crossly.

Katy chased the butterfly towards the stream, where it settled on the branch of a tree. She climbed after it, but every time she came near, the butterfly simply flew away – and then she was stuck! She looked down at the stream swirling below her.

Just then, the butterfly fluttered past her nose. Without thinking, Katy swiped at it with her paw. But as she did so, she lost her balance and went tumbling down through the tree, landing with a great *Splash!* in the water below.

"Help!" cried Katy, waving her paws wildly. Luckily she caught hold of a branch hanging over the stream and clambered onto the bank.

Katy arrived home, cold and wet. She curled up, exhausted, in front of the fire, but just as she started to doze, she felt something tugging at her whiskers. She opened one eye and saw a little mouse.

"I've done enough chasing for one day, thank you!" said Katy.

The Naughty Mermaids

Of all the mermaids that lived in the sea, Jazz and Cassandra were the naughtiest. Their latest prank was to swim to the lighthouse, call out to the little boy, Jack, who lived there, and then dive under the waves before he could see them.

One day, Jack's mum had made him a picnic as a treat. Jack laid the food on a cloth on the rocks. He had leftover pizza and crisps and fizzy drinks and chocolate.

The two naughty mermaids popped up from the waves and saw all the food.

"Hello!" they called to Jack. "Are you going to eat all this food by yourself?"

Jack was very surprised. He'd never actually *seen* the mermaids before.

"Yes," said Jack. "I mean, no! You can have some of my picnic, if you like."

The mermaids had never had pizza or crisps or fizzy drink or chocolate before. They ate so much they felt sick!

"Come back tomorrow!" called Jack, who was very excited to have met two *real* mermaids.

King Neptune was angry when he found out what Jazz and Cassandra had been doing. "Mermaids are not children!" he said. "They cannot eat children's food!"

"Humph!" said Cassandra. "I don't believe a word of it. He just wants to stop us having any fun." So the next day the two naughty mermaids swam up to the surface again to meet Jack.

The mermaids ate all Jack's food, then played hide-and-seek in the waves while Jack ran round the lighthouse trying to spot them. They came back the next day and the next. But on the fourth day, when the mermaids said goodbye and started to swim to the bottom of the sea, oh dear! Their tails had become stiff and heavy and they couldn't swim any more!

Jazz and Cassandra clung to the rocks and began to cry.

"What's wrong?" shouted Jack, alarmed.

When the mermaids explained they weren't supposed to eat children's food, Jack knew exactly what to do! He got his net and bucket and collected shrimps and seaweed from the rock pools. For three days and three nights he fed the mermaids mermaid food. By the third day they could move their tails again and swim.

When they arrived home King Neptune was waiting. But this time he wasn't angry – he was glad to see them back safely.

"I hope you two have learned a lesson," he said, quite gently. "Jack has been a good friend so you can play with him again. As long as you don't eat his food!"

There Was an Old Woman

There was an old woman who lived in a shoe.
She had so many children she didn't know what to do!
So she gave them some broth without any bread,
And she told them off
soundly and sent them to bed.

Monday's Child

Monday's child is fair of face,
Tuesday's child is full of grace,
Wednesday's child is full of woe,
Thursday's child has far to go,
Friday's child is loving and giving,
Saturday's child works hard for his living,
And the child that is born on the Sabbath day
Is bonny and blithe and good and gay.

Each Peach, Pear, Plum

Each peach, pear, plum, out goes Tom Thumb;
Tom Thumb won't do, out goes Betty Blue;
Betty Blue won't go, so out goes you.

Old King Cole

Old King Cole was a merry old soul,
And a merry old soul was he;
He called for his pipe in the middle of the night,
And he called for his fiddlers three.

Every fiddler had a very fine fiddle,
And a very fine fiddle had he;
Oh there's none so rare as can compare,
With King Cole and his fiddlers three.

Ip Dip

Ip dip, sky blue.
Who's it? Not you.
Not because you're dirty,
Not because you're clean,
My mother says you're the fairy queen.

Tom, Tom, the Piper's Son

Tom, Tom, the piper's son,
Stole a pig and away did run.
The pig was eat, and Tom was beat,
And Tom went roaring down the street.

The Farmer's in his Den

The farmer's in his den,
The farmer's in his den,
Ee–i–addio!
The farmer's in his den.

The farmer wants a wife,
The farmer wants a wife,
Ee–i–addio!
The farmer wants a wife.

The wife wants a child,
The wife wants a child,
Ee–i–addio!
The wife wants a child.

The House that Jack Built

This is the house that Jack built.

This is the malt
That lay in the house that Jack built.

This is the rat,
That ate the malt
That lay in the house that Jack built.

This is the cat,
That killed the rat that ate the malt
That lay in the house that Jack built.

This is the dog,
That worried the cat,
That killed the rat,
That ate the malt
That lay in the house that Jack built.

This is the cow with the crumpled horn,
That tossed the dog, that worried the cat,
That killed the rat, that ate the malt
That lay in the house that Jack built.

Walking in the Woods

If you hear a growl whilst walking in the woods,
It could be Mister Wolf looking for some food.
So never stop and linger, because I've got this hunch,
If you don't keep walking you could end up as...lunch!

The woods are very nice to stroll through when it's sunny.
But if you meet a wolf, you won't think it so funny!
His great big teeth are sharp, he has little else to do
Than to hide behind a tree and wait to pounce on...you!

Knights in Armour

In days gone by, or so I'm told,
The knights were **brave** and very bold.
They galloped over hill and dale,
And rescued maidens, fair and pale,
From very dangerous situations –
They were the **heroes** of the nation!

In armoured suits they went on quests,
(Of course, beneath they wore their vests),
And fought in battles far away,
From early morn 'til close of day.
And when the knights returned victorious,
Their welcome home was always **glorious!**

The Sad Princess

There was once a princess who never laughed.

"Whoever makes my daughter laugh can marry her!" said the king, who didn't know what else to do.

Lots of hopeful young men lined up to try to make the sad princess laugh.

First there was a joke-teller. *"How do you tell which end of a worm is the head? Tickle the middle and see which end laughs!"* he said. But that didn't make the princess laugh. Lots of people tried, but nobody could make the princess laugh.

The king had almost lost hope when he heard a very strange and unusual sound.

"Ha, ha! Hee, hee! Ho, ho!"

He hadn't heard it before, so it took him a while to realise that it was his daughter... **and she was laughing!**

The princess was looking out of the window at a man trying to make his donkey walk. He was pulling the donkey as hard as he could, and still the stubborn donkey would not move at all. The more the donkey refused to move, the more the princess laughed.

And so the princess and the donkey's owner were married, and they lived a happy life together, full of laughter.

A Golden Touch

There was once a king who wished that everything he touched would turn to gold.

His wish was granted by a passing fairy, and he ran around his palace turning all his belongings into gold. Vases, statues, plates and even cushions were turned to gold as soon as he touched them.

"I will be so rich," he thought.

Before long, the king started to feel hungry. "Bring me some fruit," he ordered his servant. But when the king picked up an apple, it turned to gold before it had even reached his lips.

The king began to feel very sad, but when his wife tried to comfort him with a hug, even she turned to gold.

"I never want to see gold again," sobbed the king and he wished with all his heart for things to be back to normal.

Luckily, the fairy, who had been watching all along, took pity on him. Everything changed back to the way it had been before.

The king had learned his lesson and he knew that there were many ordinary things more valuable than gold.

The Princess and the Salt

Once, a rich and powerful king summoned his three daughters to his throne room on his birthday. His first daughter gave him gold, and the second daughter brought him silver. The king was very pleased with these gifts.

"I have brought you salt," said the third daughter.

"**Salt!**" yelled the king. "How dare you insult me? What good is salt?" And he banished his own daughter from his kingdom.

But when the princess left, all the salt in the kingdom vanished. At first, the king complained that his food was tasteless, but then he became very ill from lack of salt.

The king realised how foolish he had been and sent for his daughter. When she returned to the kingdom, the salt also returned.

"Forgive me," said the king. "Your gift of salt was more precious than silver or gold, for you cannot live without salt." From that day on, the king learned to value things other than his riches.

The Straw, the Coal and the Bean

A woman was cooking beans. She lit a fire with some straw and a piece of it fell to the floor. Then she emptied the beans into the cooking pot. Plop! One dropped onto the ground beside the straw. A burning coal leapt down from the fire to join them with a crackle!

The straw, the bean and the coal congratulated themselves on escaping the fire, which would have destroyed them.

They ran through the open door and didn't stop until they reached a little brook. But there was no bridge over the water, so the straw lay across the brook and invited the others to cross. The coal leapt on first, but half way over he got scared and couldn't move. As he was still hot from the fire, he burned through the straw and they both fell into the water with a hiss!

"Ha, ha, ha!" The bean laughed so hard that she split in two, and that would have been the end of her too, if it hadn't been for a tailor who happened to be passing.

The tailor kindly sewed the bean back together again. And that is why, to this very day, some beans have a black seam!

Aladdin

Once upon a time, there was a boy called Aladdin who lived with his poor widowed mother. One evening, a strange man came to visit them.

"I am your long-lost uncle, Abanazar," he told Aladdin. He was not really Aladdin's uncle, but the wicked man knew of a magic lamp hidden in a cave, and he wanted to get his hands on it. The enchanted cave could only be entered by an innocent boy and Abanazar had chosen Aladdin for the job.

Abanazar offered Aladdin a precious ring and gave his mother food, so Aladdin agreed to help.

Abanazar took Aladdin to the cave, and told him the magic words which would open it.

"Open Sesame!" cried Aladdin. The cave opened and it didn't take Aladdin long to find the lamp. But, when he tried to leave the cave, he found that he was trapped. Aladdin rubbed his hands together to keep warm. At the same time, he rubbed the ring Abanazar had given him. There was a puff of smoke and, to his great astonishment, a genie appeared before his very eyes, for the ring was magic.

"What is your wish, oh master?" asked the genie, in a deep booming voice.

"Take me home," said Aladdin, who was still clutching the old lamp. When he got home, he polished the lamp and was amazed to see an even more powerful genie appear.

With the genie's help, Aladdin became so rich and powerful that he was able to marry a princess. But one day, Abanazar came to visit the princess. He offered her a shiny new lamp in exchange for the old one. The princess didn't know about the genie who lived in the lamp, and so she agreed.

Abanazar ran away taking Aladdin's wife with him. Aladdin could not think what to do until he remembered that he still had his old magic ring.

"Help me rescue my wife and get my lamp back," Aladdin commanded the genie of the ring.

The genie and Aladdin rescued the princess and brought back the lamp.

Aladdin was so pleased that he granted both genies their freedom.

Abanazar never troubled Aladdin and his wife again, and they lived happily ever after.

Thumbelina

There was once an old woman who wanted a daughter more than anything else in the world.

She went to see a witch who gave her a seed to plant. The seed grew into a beautiful flower and when the flower opened with a pop! a tiny little girl was sitting in the middle. The girl was no bigger than the woman's thumb, so she called her Thumbelina and loved her like a daughter.

The woman gave Thumbelina a walnut shell to sleep in and made sure she had everything she wanted. Thumbelina was very happy living with her mother.

One night, an old toad-woman passed by an open window. Hop, hoppity, hop! She saw Thumbelina as she lay asleep in her walnut shell.

"What a tiny girl," she thought to herself. "She would make a lovely bride for my son." And the toad-woman carried Thumbelina away.

Poor Thumbelina was horrified when she woke up and saw a big warty face staring at her.

"Who are you?" she gasped.

"I am Toad, and you will be my wife," said the ugly creature. And he hopped off, leaving Thumbelina stranded on a lily pad, while he and his mother set to work preparing the wedding.

Thumbelina could think of nothing worse than being married to a toad. She wept bitter tears, which fell into the river with a splash!

Some fish swam up to the surface, thinking the tear drops were insects that they could eat. When they saw the tiny girl crying her heart out, the fish took pity on her.

"Sniff! If I can't escape from here, I'll have to marry a toad," sobbed Thumbelina. The helpful fish nibbled through the stem of the lily pad, and Thumbelina floated away down the river.

The lily pad landed on a river bank near a corn field, and Thumbelina clambered off. She felt all alone in the world and began to weep again. A field-mouse scuttled past and stopped to see what was the matter.

"I am far from home," sobbed Thumbelina. "I have nobody to care for me."

The field-mouse felt very sorry for Thumbelina. He could not leave such a pretty creature crying and alone.

"Come and live with me, I'll look after you," he offered.

So Thumbelina lived underground where she was safe and warm. The field-mouse was very kind to her and they spent many happy days together.

The field-mouse's best friend was a mole, and he grew so fond of Thumbelina that he wanted to marry her. But the thought of living underground for the rest of her life made Thumbelina sad. She missed the open air and sunshine.

One day, as Thumbelina was walking through an underground passage, she saw a swallow. There seemed to be no life in the poor creature and, thinking he had died from cold, she wrapped him up.

But the bird wasn't dead. When he had warmed up he began to stir with a flitter, flutter! The swallow was very grateful to Thumbelina and wanted to help her.

"Come away with me," said the swallow. "We can fly off to a warmer land."

Thumbelina climbed onto the swallow's back, and together they flew over the bleak winter landscape until they noticed that the air was getting warmer and the land was becoming greener.

The swallow swooped down into a meadow full of flowers. Thumbelina thought it was the most beautiful place she had ever seen. The ground was thick with colourful blooms and the air was full of birds singing. The sun shone

all day long and Thumbelina felt warm and happy.

"I would like to stay here," she said. So the swallow landed, and Thumbelina jumped down from his back.

Thumbelina climbed into a lovely pink flower and breathed in its heady scent. As she looked around the meadow, she noticed that each of the flowers had a tiny sprite living in it. They were just like Thumbelina, and she felt as if she were home at last.

The king of the flower sprites flew to Thumbelina and welcomed her. When he saw Thumbelina's happy face, he fell in love and asked her to marry him. Thumbelina agreed, and they had a beautiful wedding, filled with flowers and sunshine.

Thumbelina became the queen of the flower sprites, and lived happily ever after.

Coffee and Tea

Molly, my sister, and I fell out,
And what do you think it was all about?
She loved coffee and I loved tea,
And that was the reason we couldn't agree.

There Was a Little Girl

There was a little girl,
And she had a little curl,
Right in the middle
Of her forehead.

When she was good,
She was very, very good,
But when she was bad,
She was **horrid**.

Lavender's Blue

Lavender's blue, dilly, dilly,
Lavender's green;
When I am king, dilly, dilly,
You shall be queen.

Polly, Put the Kettle On

Polly, put the kettle on,
Polly, put the kettle on,
Polly, put the kettle on,
We'll all have tea.
Sukey, take it off again,
Sukey, take it off again,
Sukey, take it off again,
They've all gone away.

Lucy Locket

Lucy Locket lost her pocket,
Kitty Fisher found it,
Not a penny was there in it,
Only ribbon round it.

Mary, Mary, Quite Contrary

Mary, Mary, quite contrary,
How does your garden grow?
With silver bells and cockle shells
And pretty maids all in a row.

Eeny, Meeny

Eeny, meeny, miney, mo,
Catch a tiger by the toe,
If he squeals let him go,
Eeny, meeny, miney, mo.

Solomon Grundy

Solomon Grundy,
Born on a Monday,
Christened on Tuesday,
Married on Wednesday,
Took ill on Thursday,
Grew worse on Friday,
Died on Saturday,
Buried on Sunday.
That was the end of
Solomon Grundy.

Two Little Dickie Birds

Two little dickie birds sitting on a wall,
One named Peter, one named Paul.
Fly away Peter, fly away Paul,
Come back Peter, come back Paul!

Five Fat Peas

Five fat peas in a pea-pod pressed,
One grew, two grew, so did all the rest.
They grew, and grew, and did not stop,
Until one day,
The pod went POP!

One, Two, Three, Four, Five

One, two, three, four, five,
Once I caught a fish alive.
Six, seven, eight, nine, ten,
Then I let it go again.
Why did you let it go?
Because it bit my finger so.
Which finger did it bite?
This little finger on the right.

One Potato, Two Potato

One potato, two potato,
Three potato, four.
Five potato,
Six potato,
Seven potato,
MORE!

Pat-a-Cake, Pat-a-Cake

Pat-a-cake, pat-a-cake, baker's man,
Bake me a cake as fast as you can.
Pat it and prick it and mark it with B,
And put it in the oven for Baby and me!
For Baby and me, for Baby and me,
Put it in the oven for Baby and me.

I'm a Little Teapot

I'm a little teapot, short and stout,
Here's my handle, here's my spout.
When I get my steam up hear me shout,
Tip me up and pour me out.

Spin, Dame

Spin, Dame, spin
Your bread you must win;
Twist the thread and break it not,
Spin, Dame, spin.

Round and Round the Garden

Round and round the garden
Like a teddy bear;
One step, two steps,
Tickle you under there!

Ride a Cock-Horse

Ride a cock-horse to Banbury Cross
To see a fine lady upon a white horse.
With rings on her fingers and bells on her toes,
She shall have music wherever she goes.

To Market, To Market

To market, to market, to buy a fat pig,
Home again, home again, jiggety-jig.
To market, to market, to buy a fat hog,
Home again, home again, jiggety-jog.
To market, to market, to buy a plum cake,
Home again, home again, market is late.
To market, to market, to buy a plum bun,
Home again, home again, market is done.

Two Princesses

Once upon a time, a long time ago, lived twin princesses called Charmina and Charlotte.

Even though they were twins, they were opposites. Princess Charmina always curtseyed politely to the king and queen. And she remained quite still while the dressmakers came to fit her new ball gown. Princess Charlotte was very different!

"Why do I have to dress like a puffball?" grumbled Princess Charlotte when it was her turn to have a new ball gown fitted.

"How dare you speak to us like that!" her parents cried.

But she did dare. She dared to run barefoot through the gardens. She dared to wear her shabbiest clothes. In fact, she didn't behave like a princess at all!

One day there was to be a ball at the palace. The guests of honour were two princes from the next kingdom.

"Why don't you go for a walk until our guests arrive?" suggested the queen to the two princesses, who were already dressed. "But stay together, don't get dirty and don't be late!"

The princesses walked to the bottom of the palace gardens. "Let's go into the forest," said Princess Charlotte.

"I don't think we should," said Princess Charmina. "Our gowns will get dirty." But Princess Charlotte had already set off.

They hadn't gone far when they heard a strange noise

coming from the next clearing.

"Let's turn back!" said Princess Charmina.

"It might be someone in distress!" said Princess Charlotte. "We have to check!"

They peeped round a tree into the clearing. In it were two horses, but there was no sign of their riders.

Then a voice called out, "Who's there?"

"Look!" said Princess Charmina. In the middle of the clearing there was a deep pit. The princesses crept up to it and peered over the edge. Princess Charmina stared in astonishment. Princess Charlotte burst out laughing. There at the bottom of the pit were the two princes.

"Well, don't just stand there," said the princes. "Get some rope from our saddlebags and help us out!"

The two princesses threw a rope down to the princes and tied the other end to the horses. Soon the princes were rescued.

Everyone enjoyed the ball that evening. The two princesses and two princes danced all night. And from that time on, Charlotte paid more attention to her gowns and hair, while Charmina became a little more playful and daring!

Oh, Bear!

There were posters all over town about the circus.

"I think I might join the circus," said Bear to his friend Rabbit.

"What would you do?" asked Rabbit.

"I'd walk the tightrope," said Bear. "It's easy peasy!"

He leapt on to the clothes line and glided gracefully. He somersaulted superbly. He bowed beautifully. Then disaster struck! He wavered and wobbled. He teetered and tottered. He lost his grip and began to slip...

"Oh, Bear!" laughed Rabbit.

"Oh, well," said Bear, as he picked himself up. "Perhaps I'll ride a unicycle instead."

"But you haven't got a unicycle," said Rabbit.

"I can fix that," said Bear. And he disappeared into his shed. Soon, Rabbit heard tools clanging and banging.

"There," called Bear, as he cycled out of the shed.

He pedalled up and down and pirouetted round and round. But then disaster struck!

"Oh, Bear!" laughed Rabbit.

"Oh, well," said Bear, as he picked himself up. "Perhaps I'll juggle instead."

"But there's nothing to juggle," said Rabbit.

"I'll find something," said Bear. And he disappeared into the kitchen. Rabbit waited patiently. He heard crockery clinking and clattering.

"There," said Bear, as he juggled down the path. He whirled the cups and twirled the plates. Higher and higher they went.

Then disaster struck! The cups and plates crashed down and the whole lot smashed.

"Oh, Bear!" laughed Rabbit. "I'm not sure the circus is a good idea."

"Nonsense!" said Bear. "Of course it is."

"But Bear," said Rabbit. "You've tried walking the tightrope. You've tried riding a unicycle. You've tried juggling. And look what happened."

"Yes," said Bear. "Look what happened. I made you laugh. Now I know exactly the right job for me." Quickly he ran indoors.

It wasn't long before he was back.

"Oh, Bear!" laughed Rabbit. "You're right. You make a perfect clown!"

The Littlest Frog

Webster was the littlest frog on Looking-Glass Pond, and every day he sat on his own, watching the other frogs play leap-frog over the water.

"Hop it, Titch!" they would croak. "You're far too small to join in our games."

"Please let me play with you," said Webster, one bright, moonlit night. "I can jump really high!"

The other frogs just laughed.

"But I can!" he insisted. He took a deep breath. "I can jump... over the moon!"

The other frogs laughed so much, they nearly fell off their lily pads.

"I'll prove it!" he said. "Just watch me."

One... two... three... *jump!* Webster leapt off his lily pad and sailed over the moon's reflection in the pond.

The other frogs stared in amazement. It was true. Webster could jump over the moon!

"We're sorry we didn't believe you," said one of the big frogs. "Of course you can play with us. You might not be the biggest frog on the pond, but you certainly are the cleverest!"

The Yellow Bluebells

The fairies at Corner Cottage were always busy looking after the flowers in the garden.

It was Blossom's job to paint the bluebells blue.

One evening, Blossom had a cold. "I don't think I can work tonight," she told her friend Petal, sniffing. "I'll have to ask the gnomes."

"No problem!" said Chip and Chuck when she asked them. "Just leave it to us."

When Blossom got up the next morning she was feeling much better – until she saw that the naughty gnomes had painted some of the bluebells… *yellow!*

"Have you seen what they've done?" she said to Petal. "What will Jamie think?"

Jamie lived in Corner Cottage. That morning when he came out to play he noticed that something looked different.

"I'm sure those flowers were blue yesterday," he thought.

"Mum," he said, going into the kitchen, "I've picked you some flowers."

"Yellowbells?" said Mum. "I don't remember planting those."

That night, Blossom painted all the bluebells blue again. When Jamie and his mum went into the garden the next morning, everything was as it should be.

"It must have been fairies!" joked Mum.

Teddy Bear, Teddy Bear

Teddy bear, teddy bear,
Touch the ground.
Teddy bear, teddy bear,
Turn around.
Teddy bear, teddy bear,
Walk upstairs.
Teddy bear, teddy bear,
Say your prayers.
Teddy bear, teddy bear,
Turn out the light.
Teddy bear, teddy bear,
Say goodnight.

An Elephant Walks

An elephant walks like this and that;
He's terribly tall and he's terribly fat.
He's got no fingers,
He's got no toes,
But goodness gracious
What a long, long nose!

This Little Piggy

This little piggy went to market,
This little piggy stayed at home,
This little piggy had roast beef,
This little piggy had none,
And this little piggy cried,
"Wee, wee, wee, wee, wee!"
All the way home.

Incy Wincy Spider

Incy Wincy Spider climbed up the spout,
Down came the rain and washed the spider out.
Out came the sun, and dried up all the rain,
Incy Wincy Spider climbed up the spout again.

The Jumblies

They went to sea in a sieve, they did,
In a sieve they went to sea.
In spite of all their friends could say,
On a winter's morn, on a stormy day,
In a sieve they went to sea!
And when the sieve turned round and round,
And everyone cried, "You'll all be drowned!"
They called aloud, "Our sieve ain't big,
But we don't care a button! We don't care a fig!
In a sieve we'll go to sea!"

Far and few, far and few,
Are the lands where the Jumblies live;
Their heads are green, and their hands are blue,
And they went to sea in a sieve.

And in twenty years they all came back,
In twenty years or more.
And everyone said, "How tall they've grown!
For they've been to the Lakes, and the Torrible Zone,
And the hills of the Chankly Bore!"
And they drank their health, and gave them a feast
Of dumplings made of beautiful yeast.
And everyone said, "If we only live,
We too will go to sea in a sieve,
To the hills of the Chankly Bore!"
Far and few, far and few,
Are the lands where the Jumblies live;
Their heads are green, and their hands are blue,
And they went to sea in a sieve.

Little Jack Jingle

Little Jack Jingle,
He used to live single:
But when he got tired of this kind of life,
He left off being single, and lived with his wife.

Harry Parry

O rare Harry Parry,
When will you marry?
When apples and pears are ripe.
I'll come to your wedding,
Without any bidding,
And dance and sing all the night.

Little Tommy Tittlemouse

Little Tommy Tittlemouse,
Lived in a little house;
He caught fishes
In other men's ditches.

Young Roger Came Tapping

Young Roger came tapping at Dolly's window,
Thumpaty, thumpaty, thump!
He asked for admittance, she answered him "No!"
Frumpaty, frumpaty, frump!
"No, no, Roger, no! As you came you can go!"
Stumpaty, stumpaty, stump!

Jack, Jack, the Bread's A-Burning

Jack, Jack, the bread's a-burning,
All to a cinder;
If you don't come and fetch it out
We'll throw you through the window.

Little Jumping Joan

Here am I, little jumping Joan.
When nobody's with me,
I'm always alone.

Hot Cross Buns!

Hot cross buns!
Hot cross buns!
One a penny, two a penny,
Hot cross buns!
If you have no daughters,
Give them to your sons.
One a penny, two a penny,
Hot cross buns!

Catch It If You Can

Mix a pancake, beat a pancake,
Put it in a pan.
Cook a pancake, toss a pancake,
Catch it if you can!

Simple Simon

Simple Simon met a pieman going to the fair;
Said Simple Simon to the pieman,
"Let me taste your ware."
Said the pieman to Simple Simon,
"Show me first your penny."
Said Simple Simon to the pieman,
"Sir, I have not any!"

Georgie Porgie

Georgie Porgie, pudding and pie,
Kissed the girls, and made them cry.
When the boys came out to play,
Georgie Porgie ran away.

Willie Wastle

I Willie Wastle,
Stand on my castle,
And all the dogs of your town,
Will not drive Willie Wastle down.

Jack Sprat

Jack Sprat could eat no fat,
His wife could eat no lean;
And so, between the two of them,
They licked the platter clean.

Mother Hulda

There was once a woman with two daughters. Her stepdaughter was hard working and beautiful, while her own daughter was ugly and lazy. The woman preferred her own daughter, and made her stepdaughter do all the work around the house.

One day, the woman gave her stepdaughter an enormous basket of wool.

"Take this wool and spin it all. Don't come back until it's finished," she told her.

So the stepdaughter sat and spun until her fingers bled. She went to wash her fingers in the well, but accidently dropped the spindle into the water. Plop!

She climbed down to find it and, when she reached the bottom of the well, she found herself in a strange land. After walking a while she reached a little house. A kind woman called Mother Hulda lived there and gave the girl food and shelter. In return, the girl helped Mother Hulda with all her chores.

But after a while, even though this woman was so much

kinder than her stepmother, she began to feel homesick. "I would like to return home," said the girl to Mother Hulda.

So Mother Hulda gave the girl back her spindle and, as the girl left the strange land, a **shower of gold** fell down and stuck to her.

When the girl arrived home, her stepmother was amazed. She wanted the same thing to happen to her own lazy daughter.

"Do just as your sister did," she told the lazy girl. But the lazy daughter could not be bothered to sit and spin, so she stuck her hands into a thorny bush to make them bleed. Then she dropped the spindle down the well and climbed in after it.

The lazy girl knocked on Mother Hulda's door and asked for food and shelter. She ate her fill and then fell asleep, **snoring** like a pig!

"Give me back my spindle. I want to go home now," said the rude girl to Mother Hulda when she woke up.

So Mother Hulda took the girl back to the bottom of the well. But instead of gold, it was **tar** that fell upon her.

The lazy girl returned to her mother who tried to scrub her clean. But the tar was stuck fast, and remained so for the rest of her life.

The Fisherman and his Wife

One day, when the sea was blue and calm, a poor fisherman set off to work. At first he caught nothing and was about to call it a day, when he felt a tug on his line. His catch pulled hard as he struggled to wind it in. "This must be a very big fish," he thought. The fish was enormous, and the fisherman was very pleased. But his pleasure turned to astonishment when the fish spoke to him.

"Please throw me back," pleaded the fish. "I am not really a fish at all, but an **enchanted prince.**"

The stunned fisherman put the fish back into the water and set off for home.

The fisherman and his wife were so poor that they lived in a pigsty. When he told his wife about the talking fish she was angry with him.

"You fool!" she said. "No wonder that we're so poor if you can't see a good thing when it's biting you on the nose!"

The fisherman's wife told him that, if the fish was an enchanted prince, he should have asked for something in return for setting him free.

"Go back to the same spot tomorrow and catch that fish again, and this time ask him for a little cottage so we can live a better life," said the fisherman's wife.

The next morning, when the sea was green and choppy, the fisherman set off again. He rowed out to the same spot as the day before, hoping to see the magical fish.

"Enchanted prince, please hear my plea, jump out from the water and talk to me," called the fisherman.

The fish appeared and asked the fisherman why he had called him. The fisherman explained that he was a very poor man and would like to live in a little cottage instead of a pigsty.

"Go home," said the fish. "Your wish is granted." And he left with a
splish!

So the fisherman returned to his wife, who waved to him from the window of their lovely new cottage.

The fisherman's wife was happy for a little while, but soon became discontented again.

"I think we could have asked for more from that magic

fish," she told her husband one evening. "This is only a small cottage, a castle would be much better." And she begged her husband to go and find the magic fish, and ask him to grant her wish.

The next morning, when the sea was purple and rough, the fisherman set off again and rowed out to the same spot as before.

"Enchanted prince, please hear my plea, jump out from the water and talk to me," called the fisherman.

The fish appeared, although he didn't seem very happy about being called again. The fisherman explained that his wife found the cottage rather small, and would prefer to live in a castle.

"Go home," said the fish. "Your wish is granted." And he left with a splash!

So the fisherman returned to his wife, who waved to him from the window of a grand castle.

But the fisherman's wife wanted even more. "If that fish can give us a grand castle, he can make me a queen," she said.

The next morning, when the sea was grey and smelly, the fisherman set off again and rowed out to the same spot as before. *"Enchanted prince, please hear my plea, jump out from the water and talk to me,"* called the fisherman.

The fish appeared, not at all pleased to be called again. The fisherman explained that his wife now wanted to be a queen.

"Go home," said the fish. "Your wish is granted." And he left with a splosh!

So the fisherman returned to his wife, who was now a queen.

"If that fish can make me a queen, then he can make me the ruler of the whole world!" said the fisherman's wife.

The next morning, when the sea was black and stormy, the fisherman set off again and rowed out to the same spot as before. *"Enchanted prince, please hear my plea, jump out from the water and talk to me,"* called the fisherman.

The fish appeared, and he was furious. The fisherman explained that his wife now wanted to be the ruler of the world. "Go home," said the fish. "Your wife has what she deserves." And he left with a splish! splash! splosh!

So the fisherman returned to his wife... who was living in the pigsty again!

The Snow Queen

Once upon a time, there was a wicked elf who made a magic mirror that showed everything in a bad light. When the mirror broke with a crack! hundreds of glass shards went flying out around the world.

Kai and Gerda were a little girl and boy who had grown up with each other and were like brother and sister.

One day, when they were playing outside, a shard of the broken mirror lodged in Kai's eye. Kai became very cold and unfriendly, and poor Gerda had no idea what had happened to him.

"Come and play with me, Kai," begged Gerda. She hoped that Kai would come to his senses and be friendly again. But Kai was bitterly cold to her, and all around him.

"I don't want to play with you any more. Leave me alone," he said.

Kai liked the cold and the ice. Snowflakes became his favourite thing of all.

He spent all day looking at

snowflakes and the pretty shapes they made.

Before long, the Snow Queen herself came to notice Kai, and one day she came to see him. "I can take you to a place where it is always cold and snowy," she told Kai. And so Kai went away with her.

Nobody knew where Kai had gone, and most people thought that he must be dead. But Gerda felt in her heart that he was still alive. She never lost faith in her old friend and vowed to find him.

Gerda set of to look for Kai wearing new red shoes. After a while she came to a river. "River, have you seen my friend Kai?" she asked. But the river would not reply. So Gerda removed her lovely red shoes, and offered them to the river.

"I will give you these new red shoes if you will help me find my friend," she told the river, and threw the shoes into the water with a splash! The river replied:

"In my murky waters deep, many secrets do I keep.
But no boy rested his head upon my muddy river bed."

Gerda was relieved to find out that Kai had not drowned, and set off again. She walked for many miles until she came to a beautiful garden where she stopped to rest.

Gerda lay down amongst the fragrant flowers, and fell asleep.

She dreamed of flowers pushing up through the soil.

When she woke up, she thought she could hear the flowers whispering to her. She listened carefully and, sure enough, a beautiful rose spoke to her:

"Beneath the ground where roots run deep,
I cannot see your friend asleep."

Gerda was happy because she knew this meant that Kai wasn't dead. She set off once more to look for her dear friend.

While Gerda was walking through a forest, she met a reindeer.

"Reindeer, have you seen my friend Kai?" she asked him.

"Is he the boy who likes snowflakes?" replied the reindeer.

"Yes, they are his favourite thing," said Gerda.

The kind reindeer told Gerda that he had seen Kai in the grounds of the Snow Queen's palace. "Climb onto my back, and I'll take you there," he said. Gerda thought her heart would burst with happiness. She felt sure that she would soon find Kai and take him home.

But when she and the reindeer reached the Snow Queen's land, they found that it was guarded by snowflakes.

"How will we ever get past these snowflakes?" thought Gerda. But as she walked through them, they were melted by the warmth of her heart. Gerda and the reindeer walked through the icy land searching everywhere for Kai.

"There he is!" said Gerda, suddenly, seeing her old friend sitting in the middle of a frozen lake. She rushed over to greet him, but when she flung her arms around him, she was heartbroken to realise that Kai did not remember who she was.

"Who are you?" said Kai. "Leave me alone." But Gerda would not let go of him. She cried so hard that Kai's icy heart began to melt. Kai started crying as well, and his own tears washed the shard of broken mirror from his eye.

"Gerda, is it really you?" asked Kai.

"Yes. I've come to take you home," said Gerda. But Kai noticed the Snow Queen riding towards them. "We must leave this place quickly," warned Kai. "The Snow Queen will freeze our hearts and make us stay here." So Kai and Gerda climbed onto the reindeer's back and rode away from the icy land. They were never parted again and lived happily ever after.

Little Jack Horner

Little Jack Horner sat in the corner,
Eating his Christmas pie;
He put in his thumb, and pulled out a plum,
And said, "What a good boy am I!"

Little Tommy Tucker

Little Tommy Tucker sings for his supper,
What shall we give him? Brown bread and butter.
How shall he cut it without a knife?
How shall he marry without a wife?

Peter, Peter

Peter, Peter, pumpkin eater,
Had a wife and couldn't keep her.
He put her in a pumpkin shell
And there he kept her, very well.

Pease Pudding Hot

Pease pudding hot, pease pudding cold,
Pease pudding in the pot, nine days old.
Some like it hot, some like it cold,
Some like it in the pot, nine days old.

Pop Goes the Weasel

Half a pound of tuppenny rice,
Half a pound of treacle.
That's the way the money goes,
Pop goes the weasel!
Up and down the city road,
In and out of the Eagle,
That's the way the money goes,
Pop goes the weasel!

Oats and Beans and Barley Grow

Oats and beans and barley grow,
Oats and beans and barley grow.
Do you or I or anyone know
How oats and beans and barley grow?

First the farmer sows his seed,
Then he stands and takes his ease.
He stamps his feet and claps his hands
And turns around to view the lands.

This Old Man

This old man, he played one;
He played knick-knack on my drum.
With a knick-knack, paddy whack,
Give a dog a bone; this old man came rolling home.

This old man, he played two;
He played knick-knack on my shoe.
With a knick-knack, paddy whack,
Give a dog a bone; this old man came rolling home.

This old man, he played three;
He played knick-knack on my knee.
With a knick-knack, paddy whack,
Give a dog a bone; this old man came rolling home.

This old man, he played four;
He played knick-knack on my door.
With a knick-knack, paddy whack,
Give a dog a bone; this old man came rolling home.

This old man, he played five;
He played knick-knack on my hive.
With a knick-knack, paddy whack,
Give a dog a bone; this old man came rolling home.

My Favourite Chair

My favourite chair is small like me,
I sit on it to watch TV.
And sometimes when I read a book
I take my chair into a nook
And sit there while I turn the pages,
I often stay like that for ages.

I know that, as the years go by,
I will grow up very high,
But my chair will stay as small
As it is now (chairs don't grow tall).
But for now I fit just right,
So I'll continue to sit tight!

A Was an Apple Pie

A was an apple pie,
B bit it,
C cut it,
D dealt it,
E eyed it,
F fought for it,
G got it,
H had it,
I inspected it,
J jumped for it,
K kept it,

L longed for it,
M mourned for it,
N nodded at it,
O opened it,
P peeped in it,
Q quartered it,
R ran for it,
S stole it,
T took it,
U upset it,
V viewed it,
W wanted it,
X, Y, Z,
All wished for
a piece in hand.

Little Bo-Peep

Little Bo-Peep has lost her sheep,
And doesn't know where to find them;
Leave them alone,
And they'll come home,
Wagging their tails behind them.

Mary Had a Little Lamb

Mary had a little lamb,
Its fleece was white as snow;
And everywhere that Mary went
The lamb was sure to go.
It followed her to school one day,
Which was against the rule;
It made the children laugh and play
To see a lamb at school.

Baa, Baa, Black Sheep

Baa, baa, black sheep, have you any wool?
Yes sir, yes sir, three bags full.
One for the master,
And one for the dame,
And one for the little boy
Who lives down the lane.

Cock-a-Doodle-Doo!

Cock-a-doodle-doo!
My dame has lost her shoe!
My master's lost his fiddling stick,
And doesn't know what to do.

Little Boy Blue

Little Boy Blue, come blow your horn.
The sheep's in the meadow,
The cow's in the corn.
Where is the boy who looks after the sheep?
He's under a haycock, fast asleep.
Will you wake him?
No, not I, for if I do, he's sure to cry.

Goosey, Goosey, Gander

Goosey, goosey, gander,
Whither do you wander?
Upstairs and downstairs
And in my lady's chamber.
There I met an old man
Who would not say his prayers,
So I took him by the left leg,
And threw him down the stairs.

Maria's Haircut

One spring day, Maria the sheep stood by the pond in Old MacDonald's farmyard, gazing sadly into the water.

"What is she doing?" whispered Doris the duck to her friend Dora. "You don't often see sheep near water."

Meanwhile, ducklings were swimming across to see who the visitor was.

"Sheep don't eat ducklings, do they?" asked Dora, anxiously.

"Of course not!" replied Doris.

Just then, Maria gave such a big sigh that she blew the ducklings right across the pond and they had to be rescued by their mothers!

"What's the trouble, my dear?" asked Old George, the horse. "Has your lamb run away again?"

"No," sighed Maria. "It isn't that. Just look at me!"

Old George looked carefully at Maria. "Well, you look even more, er, wonderfully woolly than usual," he said, gallantly.

"I look a fright," said Maria. "My coat should have been trimmed weeks ago, but Old MacDonald seems to have forgotten."

"Hmmmm. He can be a little forgetful," said Old George. "I'll speak to the other animals and see what they suggest."

"Perhaps I could nibble her coat," said Percy the pig, who would eat almost anything!

"No, we need to remind Old MacDonald to give Maria a haircut," said Poppy the cow.

"Old MacDonald is always so busy," added Henrietta the hen. "How can we make him notice Maria's problem?"

That gave Poppy a very good idea.

"It's Mrs MacDonald that notices things," she mooed thoughtfully. "Perhaps you *should* do some nibbling, Percy!"

So Percy did a little nibbling and the hens scurried away with the tufts of wool in their beaks, searching for the farmer.

When Old MacDonald went into the farmhouse for his lunch that day, Mrs MacDonald threw up her hands in horror! "MacD!" she cried. "You're covered in wool! Don't bring all those fluffy bits into my clean kitchen! It's obviously time those sheep were shorn."

The very next day, Maria's haircut was the talk of the farmyard. And she and her friends strutted happily around, looking as smart and as stylish as any sheep you've ever seen.

Sugarplum and the Butterfly

"Sugarplum," said the Fairy Queen, "I've got a very important job for you to do." Sugarplum was always given the most important work. The Fairy Queen said it was because she was the kindest and most helpful of all the fairies. "I want you to make a rose-petal ball gown for my birthday ball next week."

"It will be my pleasure," said Sugarplum happily.

Sugarplum began to gather cobwebs for the thread, and rose petals for the dress. While she was collecting the thread she found a butterfly caught in a cobweb.

"Oh, you poor thing," sighed Sugarplum. Very carefully, she untangled the butterfly, but his wing was broken. Sugarplum laid the butterfly on a bed of feathers. She gathered some nectar from a special flower and fed him a drop at a time. Then she set about mending his wing with a magic spell.

After six days, the butterfly was better. He was very grateful. But now Sugarplum was behind with her work!

"Oh dear! I shall never finish the Fairy Queen's ball gown by tomorrow," she cried. "Whatever shall I do?"

The butterfly comforted her. "Don't worry, Sugarplum," he

said. "We'll help you."

He gathered all his friends together. There were yellow, blue, red and orange butterflies. He told them how Sugarplum had rescued him from the cobweb and helped to mend his wing.

The butterflies gladly gathered up lots of rose petals and dropped them next to Sugarplum. Then the butterflies flew away to gather more cobwebs, while Sugarplum arranged all the petals. Back and forth went Sugarplum's hand with her needle and thread making the finest cobweb stitches. Sugarplum added satin ribbons and bows. When she had finished, Sugarplum was very pleased with the ball gown.

"Dear friend," she said to the butterfly, "I couldn't have finished the dress without your help."

"And I could never have flown again without your kindness and help," said the butterfly.

And the Fairy Queen was delighted with her new ball gown!

Kiss it Better

Rumpus was romping around the living room. He cartwheeled across the carpet. He turned a somersault on the sofa.

"Be careful!" called Mum. Too late! Rumpus slipped from the sofa and banged his head.

"My head hurts!" he groaned.

"Come here and I'll kiss it better," said Mum. She hugged Rumpus and planted a kiss on his forehead. "Now go and find something less rowdy to do," she said.

Rumpus rushed out into the garden and began to ride his bike. Round and round he raced.

"Watch out!" called Mum. Too late! Rumpus crashed into the corner of the wheelbarrow and grazed his knee.

"My leg hurts!" he wailed.

"Come here and I'll kiss it better," said Mum. She hugged Rumpus and planted a kiss on his knee. "Now go and find something safer to do," she said.

Rumpus ran up the grassy slope. Then he

rolled down. "Roly poly, down the hill," he sang.

"Look where you're going!" called Mum. Too late! Rumpus rolled right into the rose bush. The thorns scratched him all along his arm.

"My arm's sore!" cried Rumpus.

"Come here and I'll kiss it better," said Mum, and she planted kisses all up his arm. "Now, try and keep out of trouble," she said.

Mum went into the kitchen. "I need a break," she thought. She made a cup of tea. She cut herself a slice of cake. Then she sat down for five minutes. Just as she picked up her cup, Rumpus zoomed into the kitchen on his skateboard.

"Rumpus!" said Mum. She moved into the living room. She sat down on the sofa and picked up the paper.

Boom! Boom! Boom! In marched Rumpus, banging on his drum. Mum sighed.

"Is anything wrong?" asked Rumpus.

"I've got a headache!" said Mum.

"Never mind," smiled Rumpus, throwing his arms around her. "I'll soon kiss it better."

Cuddles to the Rescue

Cuddles was a very smart little poodle. Her hair was snowy white and fell in perfect curls. She wore a crisp red bow on top of her head. And she never went out without her sparkly jewelled collar.

But although Cuddles was the smartest, most pampered pooch around, she was not happy. You see, she didn't have any doggy friends.

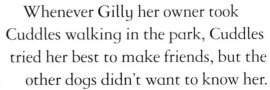

Whenever Gilly her owner took Cuddles walking in the park, Cuddles tried her best to make friends, but the other dogs didn't want to know her.

"Here comes Miss Snooty," they would bark. Then they'd point and snigger, before racing away.

And Cuddles was never let off her velvet lead. "Those other dogs look rough," explained Gilly. "You're safer with me."

Cuddles would have loved to run around with the other dogs. She thought that chasing sticks and balls looked like brilliant fun. And she was sure that she'd be able to swim in the lake if only Gilly would let her.

But the other dogs didn't know that Cuddles wanted to be one of them. They just took one look at her snowy white curls and sparkly collar and thought that she was too posh for them.

"She doesn't want to get her paws dirty," Mrs Collie

explained to Skip, her youngest pup, when he asked why Cuddles was always on a lead.

One day, Cuddles was walking with Gilly in the park when she saw Skip chasing ducks beside the lake.

"Careful!" barked Cuddles, as Skip bounced up and down excitedly. But Skip was far too busy to listen. Then Skip took an extra large bounce... into the lake!

"Help, help!" barked Skip, as he splashed about wildly in the lake. Cuddles gave a loud bark, and then, using all her strength, pulled the lead from Gilly's hand.

Cuddles was in the water in an instant. Gilly looked on in horror as Cuddles pulled the struggling pup ashore.

Once on dry land, Cuddles gave herself a big shake, then started to lick Skip dry.

"You were so brave, Cuddles!" cried Gilly.

"Will you play with me?" barked Skip, wagging his tail hopefully.

After that, Gilly always let Cuddles play with the other dogs in the park, and Cuddles was the happiest little poodle around.

Harvey the Shyest Rabbit

Harvey the rabbit was the shyest animal in the
glade beside Looking-Glass Pond. He was
too shy to talk to anyone... too shy to play
with the other animals... too shy even to
look out from behind his big floppy ears.

"There's no need to be scared," Mamma
Rabbit told him. "If you want to join in, all
you have to do is ask."

But Harvey just hid behind the long grass. No one
even noticed that he was there!

One morning, Harvey was sitting beside Looking-Glass
Pond – alone, as usual.

"I wish I could make a friend," he sighed. "But how can I,

when no one even notices me?"

Harvey gazed down sadly at
the pond. He could hardly believe
his eyes! There in the water was
another little rabbit with big floppy
ears, staring back at him.

"He looks just as scared as me!"
thought Harvey.

He waved shyly at the rabbit in the water. The water rabbit
waved too! Harvey did a bunny hop in surprise. The water
rabbit did a bunny hop.

"Hello!" said Harvey bravely, smiling.
"Hello!" said the rabbit, smiling back.
"So that's how you make friends!"
cried Harvey, in amazement. "You just
need to be a little bit brave."

He was so excited, he forgot all
about being shy or scared. Instead,
he raced off to tell everyone the
good news.

And this time, everyone
noticed him! Soon Harvey
had lots of new friends to
play with. But he never
forgot to visit his very
first friend in Looking-
Glass Pond!

Mermaid Dreams

I wish I was a mermaid
Swimming beneath the sea.
My **pet** would be a dolphin
Who'd swim along with me.

We'd play among the coral,
And in and out of caves.
If we felt quite brave enough,
We'd **peep** above the waves.

Perhaps my wish will not come true,
I'll have to wait and see.
But if you ever see a mermaid,
Please wave – it might be **me!**

Hickety Pickety

Hickety Pickety, my black hen,
She lays eggs for gentlemen;
Sometimes nine, and sometimes ten,
Hickety Pickety, my black hen!

Marking Time

Tick! Tock!
That's the clock
Marking time for me.
Every tick
And every tock,
Sets each second free.

Hickory, Dickory, Dock

Hickory, dickory, dock,
The mouse ran up the clock.
The clock struck one,
The mouse ran down,
Hickory, dickory, dock.

A Sailor Went to Sea

A sailor went to sea, sea, sea.
To see what he could see, see, see.
But all that he could see, see, see,
Was the bottom of the deep blue sea, sea, sea.

Have you ever, ever, ever,
In your long-legged life,
Met a long-legged sailor
With a long-legged wife?

No, I never, never, never,
In my long-legged life,
Met a long-legged sailor
With a long-legged wife!

Have you ever, ever, ever,
In your pigeon-toed life,
Met a pigeon-toed sailor
With a pigeon-toed wife?

No, I never, never, never,
In my pigeon-toed life,
Met a pigeon-toed sailor
With a pigeon-toed wife!

This is the Way

This is the way we wash our hands,
Wash our hands, wash our hands.
This is the way we wash our hands
On a cold and frosty morning.

This is the way we wash our face,
Wash our face, wash our face.
This is the way we wash our face
On a cold and frosty morning.

This is the way we brush our teeth,
Brush our teeth, brush our teeth.
This is the way we brush our teeth
On a cold and frosty morning.

This is the way we comb our hair,
Comb our hair, comb our hair.
This is the way we comb our hair
On a cold and frosty morning.

This is the way we wave goodbye,
Wave goodbye, wave goodbye.
This is the way we wave goodbye
On a cold and frosty morning.

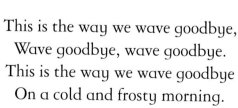

Aiken Drum

There was a man lived in the moon,
Lived in the moon, lived in the moon,
There was a man lived in the moon,
And his name was Aiken Drum.

And he played upon a ladle,
A ladle, a ladle,
He played upon a ladle,
And his name was Aiken Drum.

And his hat was made of good cream cheese,
Of good cream cheese, of good cream cheese,
And his hat was made of good cream cheese,
And his name was Aiken Drum.

And his coat was made of good roast beef,
Of good roast beef, of good roast beef,
And his coat was made of good roast beef,
And his name was Aiken Drum.

And his buttons were made of penny loaves,
Of penny loaves, of penny loaves,
And his buttons were made of penny loaves,
And his name was Aiken Drum.

Five Fat Sausages

Five fat sausages sizzling in the pan,
All of a sudden one went **bang!**

Four fat sausages sizzling in the pan,
All of a sudden one went **bang!**

Three fat sausages sizzling in the pan,
All of a sudden one went **bang!**

Two fat sausages sizzling in the pan,
All of a sudden one went **bang!**

One fat sausage sizzling in the pan,
All of a sudden it went **bang!**

And there were no sausages left!

Bookworm

Bookworm is the nickname that my mother gave to me,
Because I'd rather read a book than watch things on TV.
I like to read a story when I'm **curled** up snug in bed,
I often put away my toys and read a book instead.

A good **adventure** story is the kind that I like best,
With knights in gleaming armour saving maidens in distress.
Or sometimes I will read a book about geography,
And learn about the big wide world with many things to see.

A book is like a best friend, to take along with me.
Whatever I am doing and wherever I may be,
I'll pick up my latest read and open up the pages,
And, if nobody **bothers** me, I'll sit and read for ages!

Whoops-a-Daisy!

Clumsy elf, it's not your fault
That your fingers fumble.
The other elves all laugh at you
When you start to bumble.
You're only trying to help out –
I wish that they could see,
That you always do your best
Whatever that may be!

Whoops-a-daisy! Clumsy elf!
You're sliding in the snow!
It's not your fault if you're no good,
At watching where you go.
You're trying to stay upright,
But the snow lies in great mounds,
You do your best to hold on tight,
But – CRASH! you hit the ground.

The Wolf and the Seven Young Kids

An old mother goat lived with her seven little kids. One day she went out and left them alone, warning them that the wolf might come, and they must not let him in.

"Don't let that rascal trick you," she said. "He has a gruff old voice and his paws are as black as coal. That is how you will recognise him."

Sure enough, not long after the mother goat had left, there was a knock, knock, knock! at the door.

"Let me in," said a gruff old voice.

"We know it's you, wolf," said the kids. "You have such a gruff old voice."

So the wolf went away and ate some chalk to soften his voice. Then he went back to the goats' house and knocked on the door.

"Let me in," he said with his smooth, chalky voice. But the seven young kids noticed his black paws peeping through a crack in the bottom of the door. "We know it's you, wolf," said the kids. "Your paws are as black as coal."

So the wolf went away and covered his paws with white flour. Then he went back to the goats' house and knocked on the door.

"Let me in," he said. His voice was not gruff and

his paws were not black, so the seven young kids opened the door and let him in.

Gulp! The wolf ate six young kids, but the seventh young kid hid in a cupboard.

When the mother goat returned home, the seventh kid ran out from the cupboard and told her all about the wolf.

"Oh, my poor babies!" cried the mother goat. "We must go and find that wicked wolf." And they set off to look for him.

They found the old rascal sleeping beneath a tree. The mother goat carefully cut open the wolf's big fat stomach with a snip, snip! and six young kids hopped out alive and well!

Then she picked up six stones and put them in the wolf's stomach before sewing it back up again.

They all hid behind a tree and watched.

The wolf woke up feeling thirsty and went to get some water from the well. But the weight of the stones made him fall down the well, and he landed in the water with a splash! And he was never seen again.

The mother goat and her kids danced all the way home!

The Worn-out Dancing Shoes

There was once a king with twelve beautiful daughters.

Every morning the princesses' dancing shoes were worn right through and the king did not know why. He promised the hand in marriage of one of his daughters to any man who could solve the mystery. Many men tried and failed.

One day, a wounded soldier was walking through the kingdom. He met an old woman who told him about the princesses and said that he should try to solve the puzzle.

"When the princesses bid you goodnight, they will bring you a glass of wine. It is a sleeping potion and you must not drink it," warned the old woman. She also gave him a magic cloak that would make him invisible.

The soldier arrived at the palace and was shown to a bedroom next door to the twelve princesses. When the princesses came to say goodnight, they gave him a glass of wine, but he didn't drink it. He put on his cloak and became invisible, just in time to see the princesses disappearing down through the floor and into a secret passage.

The soldier followed them to a lake where he saw twelve princes, each waiting in a rowing boat. The princesses climbed aboard and the soldier jumped in behind the youngest.

"The boat feels heavy tonight," remarked the prince.

On the other side of the lake was a beautiful land. The trees were made of silver and jewels. The soldier took a twig to take back to the king. When he snapped off the twig, it made a **cracking** sound.

"What was that noise?" asked a prince. But nobody else had heard.

The princesses and princes soon reached a hall, where there was music playing, and they began to dance. The soldier joined in, but he was clumsy and trod on one of the princesses' toes.

"**Ow!** How clumsy you are tonight," she said to her prince. The dancing continued until dawn, when they returned home. The soldier noticed that the princesses had worn out their dancing shoes yet again.

At breakfast, the soldier showed the king the silver twig and explained what had happened. The princesses could not deny the truth and so the mystery was solved.

The soldier married the oldest princess, who was anyway rather tired of dancing, and they lived happily ever after.

The Wedding of Mrs Fox

Mrs Fox was feeling very sad because her husband had died.

"Don't be so sad," said her maid, who was a cat. "You'll soon find someone else to marry." But Mrs Fox wasn't so sure.

"I'll never find another husband as good as Mr Fox," she sighed. "He had such fine **red stockings** and such a lovely **pointed mouth.**"

One day, the maid knocked on Mrs Fox's door.

"Here's Mr Badger to see you," she said. And in came Mr Badger. Mrs Fox could not deny that he had lovely black and white stripes, but he did not have fine red stockings or a lovely pointed mouth. So, when he asked Mrs Fox to be his wife, she turned him down.

One day, the maid knocked on Mrs Fox's door again. "Here's Mr Squirrel to see you," she said. And in came Mr Squirrel.

Mrs Fox admired Mr Squirrel's lovely bushy tail, but he did not have fine red stockings or a lovely pointed mouth. So when he begged her to marry him, Mrs Fox said that she would rather not.

One day, the maid knocked on Mrs Fox's door yet again. "Here's Mr Mouse to see you," she said. And in came Mr Mouse.

"Mrs Fox had to admit that he did have a rather attractive pointed mouth, but no fine red stockings. So when he popped the question, Mrs Fox was flattered, but still refused him.

One day, the maid knocked on Mrs Fox's door yet again. "There's a young man to see you," she said. And in came a handsome fox. He had a beautiful pointed mouth, and very fine red stockings. The handsome fox came to visit Mrs Fox every day, and they fell in love.

"Mrs Fox, will you be my bride?" asked the handsome fox.

"Yes!" replied Mrs Fox. And they lived happily ever after.

The Cockerel King

There was once a very boastful king who would show off at
the slightest opportunity. If he had a new robe, he would strut
around the palace showing it off. "Look at my fine new robe.
It's made of the finest silk and fur," he would say.

"Look at you, strutting around just like a cockerel," his
wife would think.

One day, a pedlar came to the palace to sell his wares.
"Here's just the thing for such a fine fellow as you," the pedlar
told the king, as he showed him a carved wooden mirror.

The king bought the mirror and went to sit on his throne
to look at himself. But he didn't know that the mirror was a
magic one. When he looked into it, he was surprised to see a
proud cockerel staring back at him.

"This is outrageous," the king thought to himself, "I

demand a refund!" But when he tried
to get down from his throne, he
found that he was no longer a man,
but a fine feathered cockerel.

Just then, his butler came in and
saw a cockerel strutting around, so
he chased it outside. The king tried to
protest, but his words came out as a
loud cock-a-doodle-doo!

Outside the palace, the cockerel king
began to crow, and he did not stop

until his wife looked out of the window.

"Be quiet, you old cockerel," she called down to him. "Isn't it enough that I have to listen to my boastful husband crowing all day long without your dreadful noise?"

The cockerel king at once fell silent. He hadn't realized what the queen had thought of him until that very moment.

"I suppose I am rather a show-off," he thought sadly to himself. "I will change my ways if only I can be a man again."

Suddenly, there was a flash of light and the king was himself once more. He went back to the throne room and carefully picked up the mirror without looking at himself, and locked it safely away. The king did change his ways from then on and was careful not to boast or show off too much, but he never dared to look in the magic mirror again – just in case!

The Magic Pear

Once upon a time, a farmer's daughter looked up at an old pear tree and noticed that one pear on the tree was different from all the others. It was larger and had a golden tone to it. She wanted to eat it but it was too high to reach.

As she gazed hungrily up at the unusual pear, a gust of wind blew it down to her. She bit into the golden fruit and it tasted more delicious than any pear she had ever tasted.

As she swallowed the first bite, a **strange** thing happened. The girl saw a vision of herself, and she was dressed as a queen. She laughed at such a ridiculous idea. How could a farmer's daughter become a **queen?**

The next day, a handsome man rode by her farm, and he fell off his horse. The farmer's daughter looked after him until he had fully recovered. During the time she spent nursing him, they fell in love.

"Come back to my palace and be my queen," said the handsome man, who in all the time he had been there, had not told the girl he was a king.

And so the farmer's daughter became a queen and lived happily ever after.

The Genie

Once, a lazy servant girl was polishing a silver jug when, to her surprise, a genie appeared.

"**I will grant you three wishes,**" he said.

"I wish that this silver was clean," said the servant girl. She looked back down at the silver and saw that it was **gleaming** and clean.

The next day the servant girl was sewing clothes and decided to use her second wish.

"I wish that this sewing was finished," she said. She looked at the sewing and saw that it was done.

Fed up with hard work, the girl wished that she was no longer a servant. Her third wish came true at once. She was no longer a servant. The girl had become a beggar on the streets.

The girl began to cry at her terrible mistake. The genie took pity on her and appeared in a puff of smoke.

"In future, be **careful** what you wish for," said the genie. And he sent her back to her life as a servant. The girl did her work more happily from then on.

The Sun and the Wind

The sun and the wind were arguing one day.

"I am **stronger** than you," said the sun.

"What rubbish," said the wind. "I am far stronger than you."

"See that man down there?" the sun asked the wind, "I am so strong that I bet I could get that coat off him."

"You're not strong enough to do that," said the wind. "I could easily get that coat off him."

"Alright," said the sun. "You go first."

So the wind **blew** with all his might and strength. Leaves blew off the trees and tiles blew off the roof tops. But the man only pulled his coat more tightly around him. The wind could not get the coat off the man.

"Now it's my turn," said the sun. And he **shone** down on the man. The strength of the sun was so fierce that the man quickly became very hot. He became so hot that he took off his coat and slung it over his shoulder.

"I win!" said the sun.

"Oh, blow!" said the wind.

The Three Wishes

It was Princess Felicity's birthday and the royal magician had granted her three wishes.

She knew at once what her first wish would be.

"I wish I had long, golden hair," she said. Right away her hair started to grow... and grow... and **grow**. It wouldn't stop!

"I wish I had a pair of scissors," she said. And in the twinkling of an eye, a pair of scissors appeared. Princess Felicity cut her hair, but the more she cut it the more it grew.

Princess Felicity's hair was getting out of control. Soon the whole room would be filled with the golden hair. Something had to be done, quickly.

"I wish I had my old hair back again," she said. And in a flash she had her hair back as it always had been.

"I'll never moan about my hair again," said the little princess.

Princess Felicity still enjoyed her birthday. The royal wig-maker collected up all the golden hair that the princess had cut off, and used it to make a **beautiful** golden wig. Now Princess Felicity could have long, golden hair whenever she felt like a change – it hadn't been such a **bad hair** day after all!

Jelly on the Plate

Jelly on the plate,
Jelly on the plate,
Wibble wobble,
Wibble, wobble,
Jelly on the plate.

Sweeties in the jar,
Sweeties in the jar,
Shake them up,
Shake them up,
Sweeties in the jar.

Candles on the cake,
Candles on the cake,
Blow them out,
Blow them out,
Puff, puff, puff!

Jack and Guy

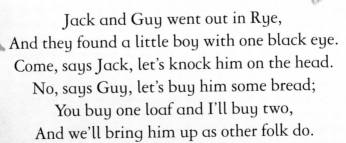

Jack and Guy went out in Rye,
And they found a little boy with one black eye.
Come, says Jack, let's knock him on the head.
No, says Guy, let's buy him some bread;
You buy one loaf and I'll buy two,
And we'll bring him up as other folk do.

I Scream

I scream, you scream,
We all scream for ice cream!

A Peanut

A peanut sat on the railway track,
His heart was all a-flutter;
Along came a train – the 9.15 –
Toot! Toot! Peanut butter!

Dibbity, Dibbity, Dibbity, Doe

Dibbity, dibbity, dibbity, doe,
Give me a pancake and I'll go.
Dibbity, dibbity, dibbity, ditter,
Please give me a lovely fritter.

Ten Green Bottles

Ten green bottles, standing on a wall,
Ten green bottles, standing on a wall,
And if one green bottle should accidentally fall,
There'd be nine green bottles, standing on a wall.

A Windy Day

On sunny days we play outside,
On rainy days we shelter.
On snowy days we wear warm clothes
And when it's hot, we swelter!

Of all the weather that exists,
The kind that I like best,
Without a doubt are windy days,
South, north, east or west.

Any way the wind can blow
Will be just fine for me,
Because my favourite thing to do
Is flying kites, you see.

So blow wind, blow – I will not mind
If you howl day and night.
While others hold onto their hats,
I'll be flying kites!

The Big, Red Train!

Peep! Peep! The whistle's blowing,
The bright green light is glowing,
The big, red train is going,
Toot! Toot! We're on our way!

Chug! Chug! The wheels are turning,
The red hot coal is burning,
And now my heart is churning,
Let's ride along all day!

But soon we're at the station,
It's time to put the brakes on,
We've reached our destination.
Hip! Hip! Hip! Hooray!

Slow Down, Bruce

On Old MacDonald's farm, no one works harder than Bruce the farm dog – except, of course, Old MacDonald! All day long, Bruce dashes around the farm, keeping an eye on everything that goes on. So, when Bruce stayed in his kennel one morning with his head on his paws, everyone began to worry.

"It's not like him at all," clucked Henrietta the hen.

"He can hardly open his eyes," purred Milly the cat.

"I've never known him have a day's illness in his life," said Old George the horse, "and I remember him as a pup."

Old MacDonald was more worried than any of them.

"Just stay there, old boy," he said gently. "I'll get someone to help you." And he hurried off to call the vet.

The vet arrived very quickly. She too was very fond of Bruce.

She carefully examined him, lifting his paws one by one, and checking every part of him thoroughly. Then she patted

the old dog's head and said, "You're like your master. You need to stop dashing around so much and take better care of yourself. You'll be fine in a day or two, but just slow down, Bruce. Take it easy for once, please."

Bruce nodded his head gratefully and went back to sleep.

Now, Mrs MacDonald had been listening, and returned to the farmhouse with a thoughtful look on her face.

Bruce did as he was told, and by the end of the week he was as right as rain – it would soon be time to go back to work.

When he saw Old MacDonald rushing through the yard, hurrying to finish a job, Bruce dashed after him.

But Mrs MacDonald rushed out of the farmhouse and called to the farmer.

"Husband!" she cried. "Did you hear what the vet said about Bruce? You must set him a good example! Please be a little more thoughtful!"

So Old MacDonald began to slow down, and so did Bruce. The sheepdog soon felt better for it – and so did Old MacDonald. And Mrs MacDonald, who had been begging her husband to take it easy for years, felt very happy indeed.

Small and Pink

One morning, Percy the pig strutted proudly through the farmyard.

"Today's the day," he told everyone he passed.

"What is he on about?" asked Doris the duck.

"Percy is expecting some piglets," clucked Jenny the hen.

"I didn't think boy pigs could have babies," said Doris, looking puzzled.

"No, no," Jenny clucked, flapping her wings. "They are coming from another farm to live here as part of his family."

Percy had tripped and trotted from one end of the farmyard to the other more times than he cared to remember, but Farmer Brown still hadn't returned with the new arrivals.

Percy went back to his sty and checked it one more time. It was spotless. The straw was piled up neatly along one wall and the water trough was clean and full.

"I must make sure that everything is ready for my piglets," said Percy, brushing a speck of dust from the doorway.

Just as Percy finished cleaning, brushing and tidying he heard Farmer Brown's truck rumbling into the farmyard – they were here at last!

Percy was so excited! He hurried from his sty, but before he could reach the truck…

Whoosh! Something very small, very pink and very fast shot past his nose.

Whizzz! Something just as small and pink and even faster

scuttled under his tail.

Wheeeee! Another small and pink and noisy thing zoomed straight under Percy's tummy.

"Eeeeeeeee!" shrieked seven little piglets, dashing in every direction around the farmyard.

Late that night, a very tired Percy stood at the doorway of his sty – it was a tip. The straw was everywhere and the water trough was upside down. But seven little piglets were fast asleep in the corner.

"They never stand still, do they?" said Jasmine the sheep.

"No," sighed Percy.

"Are you having second thoughts, Percy?" asked Old Harry the horse.

But Percy gave the kind of grin that only a very happy, contented and proud pig can give. *"Shhhhhhh!"* he whispered. "My babies are sleeping!"

The Rainy Day

Rain! It splashed on the windows, gurgled down the drainpipes, and made puddles all over the yard. And Danny and Rosie were bored. Bored, bored, bored!

Out in the pigsty, Bessie and her piglets wallowed in a giant mud bath. It was such fun! There were squeals of delight.

On the pond, the ducks bobbed along looking pleased with themselves. Rain was just water off a duck's back!

Down by the bridge, the river was rising higher and higher. Eventually, it spilled over its banks and brown muddy water flowed across the road and under the farm gate.

Joe was busy fixing the tractor in the barn when he heard a shout from the road and saw Jack the postman struggling through the water on his bike.

"Help, Joe! I'm stranded!" called Jack.

"Don't worry, Jack," Joe shouted back. "We'll get you across."

Joe put down his tools and climbed up into the tractor cab. He started the engine and reversed out of the barn.

Rosie and Danny came out of the house in their waterproofs and ran down to the bridge with Conker the dog.

"Look," gasped Rosie. "The ducklings are swimming all over the garden. And Jack's trapped by the flood!"

Joe rumbled up in the tractor. "Get on the trailer," he shouted to the children. "I'll reverse it through the flood."

"Nice weather for ducks," puffed Jack, as he scrambled aboard. "Thanks, kids. Oh, no! There goes my cap!"

Conker barked wildly and jumped in after it.

"Come back, Conker," cried Rosie. "You'll be swept away!"

"No he won't, silly," said Danny. "Conker's a champion swimmer. Go fetch it, boy!"

Conker grabbed the postman's cap in his mouth, and paddled back to the trailer. He dropped it and wagged his tail.

"Good old Conker!" shouted everyone. "Well done, boy!" Conker shook himself furiously, spraying them all with water.

Joe drove back to the yard and they all jumped off the trailer.

"Thank you, everyone," said Jack, picking up his cap. "Especially you, Conker. I'm very fond of this old cap."

"Come inside," called Mum. "You're all wet through. And what a lot of excitement for a wet Tuesday morning!"

"Brave dog," said Danny, giving Conker a pat.

The Ant and the Grasshopper

Grasshopper was a lively, happy insect, who didn't have a care in the world. He spent the long summer days relaxing in the sunshine or bouncing and dancing through the grass.

"Why are you working so hard?" asked Grasshopper one day, when he saw Ant struggling to carry some grain on her back. "It's such a sunny day! Come and play!"

"I've got no time, Grasshopper," said Ant. "I have to take this grain back to my nest, so that my family and I have enough food when winter comes. Have you built your nest yet?"

"Nest?" laughed Grasshopper. "Who needs a nest when life in the great outdoors is so wonderful? And there's plenty of food – why should I worry?"

Day after day, Grasshopper played, while Ant worked. Soon the trees began to lose their leaves and the days began to get shorter and cooler. But lazy Grasshopper hardly noticed. He was still too busy enjoying himself.

A few days later, it began to snow. Grasshopper suddenly found himself cold and all alone. He was hungry and there wasn't a crumb of food to be found anywhere!

"I know," said Grasshopper. "Ant will help me." So he set out

to look for Ant's nest. It was safe and warm beneath a rock.

Ant came out to see him. "What do you want?" she asked.

"Please, Ant," said Grasshopper, "have you any food to spare?"

Ant looked at him. "All summer long, while we worked hard to gather food and prepare our nest, what did you do?"

"I played and had fun, of course," said Grasshopper. "That's what summer is for!"

"Well, you were wrong, weren't you," said Ant. "If you play all summer, then you must go hungry all winter."

"Yes," said Grasshopper sadly, as a tiny tear fell from the corner of his eye. "I've learned my lesson now. I just hope it isn't too late!"

Ant's heart softened. "Alright, come on in," she said. "I'll find some food for you."

Grasshopper gratefully crawled into the warm nest, where Ant and her family shared their food with him.

By the time spring came around, Grasshopper was fat and fit and ready to start building a nest of his very own!

Bedtime with Gran

When I snuggle up at night,
There's no one that I'd rather
Tuck me in all nice and tight
Than my dear grandmother.

"Which story would you like to read?"
My sweet old gran will say.
I always pick the longest one
To make sure that she stays.

She takes me to another world
Of fairies, queens and kings.
And when she kisses me goodnight,
I dream wonderful things.

A Snowy Day

On this chilly winter's day,
My breath hangs in the air,
Frozen in this snowy scene,
I watch it linger there.

A glistening carpet covers all,
Turning the green grass white,
And crunches with each footstep,
A wintery delight!

First I'll make snow angels,
And then a snowman, too.
And last of all, you guessed it –
A snowball-fight with you!

Favourite Things

I've written down a list
Of all my favourite things;
Rainbows and fairy cakes
And butterfly wings.

A journey on a train,
A visit from a friend,
Candyfloss and ice cream –
The list might never end!

Each time I think of one,
I add it to the rest,
It's fun to keep a track
Of things that I like best.

I roll it in a scroll,
And keep it safe from harm,
My list of favourite things
Is longer than my arm!

My Grandpa's Trunk

A wooden chest stands on the floor,
Just inside my grandpa's door.
What hidden secrets does it hold?
Perhaps he has some pirate's gold!

Grandpa, I ask, please may I see
What's inside? He looks at me
With his kind old twinkling eyes,
And says I'm in for a surprise!

He carefully opens up the trunk,
I hear the big old lock go clunk!
The lid is open, eagerly
I look inside and what I see...

Is Grandpa's treasure! Nothing gold,
No sparkling diamonds to behold,
But lots of books and this and that,
Worn-out clothes, and an old straw hat.

Fields of Gold

When the summer's over
And the sun is losing heat,
The rolling fields around me
Are full with ripened wheat.

A glowing golden carpet
Gently swaying as it stands,
Waiting for the farmer
To harvest from his land.

When the grains are gathered
And the straw lies on the ground,
We'll bale it and then stack it
Into lovely golden mounds.

Sleepyheads

Where do you go to, sleepyheads,
When you're fast asleep?
We drift away in a silver shell
In our slumber, deep.

What do you dream of, Sleepyheads,
In your beautiful silver shell?
We dream of grassy meadows
And a magic wishing-well.

What do you hope for, sleepyheads,
When you make your wishes?
We wish to see a mermaid
And some flying fishes.

The Princess Who Would Not Speak

There was once a princess who wouldn't speak. Her mother offered her **wonderful** treats to try to persuade her to talk, but still she wouldn't utter a word.

One day, the king offered a bag of gold coins to the person who could make his daughter speak. People lined up to try their luck, but nobody could make her talk.

An old peasant woman came to hear of the reward. She put a **chicken** on her head and set off to the palace, getting a few funny looks on the way.

When the old woman met the princess, she made small talk, but never once mentioned the chicken on her head. After some time, the hen gave a **squawk** and laid an egg which fell to the ground with a **splat!** The old woman continued to talk about this and that, as if nothing had happened.

The princess couldn't stop herself. "Did you know that you have a **chicken** on your head?" she asked. The king was delighted and paid the old woman a bag of gold. She and her chicken went home happy.

The Prince and the Peasant

Once there was a young prince who wanted to go exploring. By chance, he met a peasant boy who looked **exactly** like him. He realised that, if they swapped clothes, he would get his wish. The peasant boy agreed and, as soon as they swapped, the prince felt a hand on his shoulder. "There you are lad," said a **gruff** voice.

The prince was led away and put to work in a field. It was hard work and by the time he had finished he was very **hungry.** But all he got for his supper was a thin soup and a crust of bread.

The next day, the prince and the boy changed back into their own clothes. "When I am king, I promise to make sure that nobody goes hungry," he told the boy.

The prince grew up and, when he was king, he did not forget his promise.

The Princess and the Moon

There was once a princess who got everything she wanted right away. But one day, the princess asked her father for something impossible.

"Daddy, can I have the moon?" she asked.

Her father tried everything to bring down the moon, but nothing worked. "I'm afraid you can't have the moon because it is too big to bring down from the sky," the king told his daughter.

"But when I look at it, it's just a tiny silver ball no bigger than my thumbnail," replied the puzzled princess. So the king asked his silversmith to make a tiny silver moon, which he gave to his daughter.

"Thank you, Daddy, it's so beautiful," she said.

When the moon appeared in the sky that night, the king was worried she would realise her moon wasn't the real one. But the princess didn't mind.

"The moon has grown back again, of course," she said. "It's always growing and shrinking!'

The Joker Prince

There was once a prince who was always playing tricks on people. Once, he balanced a bucket of water over the kitchen door and the bucket tipped over and soaked the chef. Everyone was fed up with the prince's practical jokes.

But one day, the prince met his match. There was a princess visiting the palace and the prince had placed a whoopee cushion on her chair at breakfast. The princess was very annoyed and vowed to pay him back.

The princess could throw her voice to sound as if it was coming from another direction. That afternoon, when the prince was playing with his dog, she hid and threw her voice to make it sound as if the dog was talking. "I suppose you think your tricks are funny," the dog appeared to say.

"W-w-what?" stuttered the prince. He couldn't believe his ears.

"Stop being such a pain," the voice went on. "Nobody likes your tricks."

The prince was so shocked that he stopped playing tricks on people. He spent many hours coaxing his dog to talk again, but he never succeeded!

The Princess and the Fool

There was once a rich fool who had a very clever servant. The rich fool came to hear of a princess who wanted to marry a clever man. Thinking himself to be clever, he went to see her.

The princess decided to see how clever the rich fool was.

"If a cockerel laid an egg on top of a hill, which side of the hill would it roll down?" she asked.

The fool went away and, after a day of rolling eggs down a hill, he felt sure he knew the answer.

As the rich fool began to tell the princess, his servant began to laugh. He laughed so much he couldn't stop.

"What's so funny?" asked the puzzled fool.

"The egg wouldn't roll down either side of the hill. Cockerels do not lay eggs – hens do!"

The princess decided that the servant was clever and also very funny – so she married him instead! And they lived a happy life filled with laughter.

The Princess and the Donkey

There was once a very bossy princess who always got her own way, and if she didn't – she would **scream** until she did.

One day, she was walking in her rose garden when she found a donkey had strayed into it.

"Get out of my garden!" she shouted at the donkey. But the donkey did not budge. The princess started to scream, but the donkey just folded in his ears and stood firm. The princess was **furious** and tried everything to make the donkey leave her garden, but the donkey would not go.

By the time the donkey's owner came along, the princess was red in the face with anger. The donkey's owner gave his creature a gentle stroke on its head.

"Come on girl," said the donkey's cheerful owner, and the cheeky beast happily followed him out of the rose garden.

Laughing merrily, the owner called back over his shoulder, "You only had to ask nicely!"

The princess should have learned her lesson after this, but I'm afraid to say that she did not!

Goldilocks and the Three Bears

Once upon a time, Goldilocks was playing in the woods near her home. Her beautiful long, blonde curls tumbled down her back as she skipped along the path. Goldilocks stopped and sniffed the air… she could smell something **yummy!**

Feeling hungry, Goldilocks followed the trail and soon found herself in front of a little house.

"How sweet," she cried, clapping her hands in delight. "I wonder who lives here…"

Goldilocks knocked loudly on the front door. Nobody was at home but the door was unlocked, so Goldilocks went in. She saw a kitchen table with three bowls on it. "I'm sure no one will mind if I just have a little taste of this porridge," she told herself. Goldilocks picked up a spoon and started to eat from the biggest bowl of porridge.

"**Yuck!**" she cried, shaking her golden hair. "This porridge is far too salty!"

Goldilocks tried the medium-sized bowl.

"Yuck!" she gasped. "This porridge is far too sweet!"

There was still the small bowl to try. Goldilocks took a little mouthful. "Mmmm!" she sighed, licking her lips. "This porridge is perfect!" And she ate it all up.

Yawn! Goldilocks began to feel sleepy. In the living room, she saw three armchairs.

There was a big chair, a medium-sized chair and a tiny little chair.

Goldilocks climbed onto the biggest chair. "This chair is too big!" she sighed.

Next, Goldilocks clambered onto the medium-sized chair. "This chair is a bit too lumpy!" cried Goldilocks.

Then, Goldilocks tried the tiny chair. "This chair is perfect!" beamed Goldilocks happily. She wiggled and jiggled around to get even more comfy when… Cr-r-r-ack! The chair broke into little pieces.

"Oh, no!" Goldilocks gasped. "Maybe I'll find somewhere else to lie down instead." And so Goldilocks walked up the stairs as bold as brass.

Upstairs, Goldilocks found three beds. There was a big bed, a medium-sized bed and a tiny little bed.

Goldilocks jumped up and down on each bed.

The big bed was too hard, the medium-sized bed was too soft, and the little bed was… "Perfect!" Goldilocks sighed happily. And the little girl crawled under the covers and fell fast asleep.

Meanwhile, three hungry bears returned to the house in the wood. They had been for a walk while their hot porridge cooled down. But the door was wide open and there were muddy footprints inside. The bears followed the footprints into the kitchen, and saw at once that someone had been there.

"Who's been eating my porridge?" growled Daddy Bear.

"Who's been eating my porridge?" gasped Mummy Bear.

"Who's been eating my porridge," squeaked Baby Bear, "and eaten it all up?"

Feeling shocked and confused, the three bears padded into the living room and saw that someone had been there, too.

"Who's been sitting in my chair?" roared Daddy Bear.

"Who's been sitting in my chair?" growled Mummy Bear.

"Who's been sitting in my chair,'" yelped Baby Bear, "and broken it?"

Suddenly, the three bears heard snoring from upstairs.

Daddy Bear, Mummy Bear and Baby Bear rushed up the stairs and went into the bedroom.

"Who's been sleeping in my bed?" roared Daddy Bear.

"Who's been sleeping in my bed?" growled Mummy Bear.

"Who's been sleeping in my bed," squeaked Baby Bear, pointing to Goldilocks, "and is still there?"

Goldilocks woke up with a start and found three bears peering down at her.

She jumped out of bed, ran out of the house and through the woods as fast as she could.

And the three bears never saw Goldilocks again.

The Enchanted Apple Tree

There was once an enchanted apple tree that only gave fruit once every ten years and, when it did, villagers came to pick the delicious apples and **make a wish.**

There was a little girl in the village called Pomona. She had heard all about the tree but had never tasted its delicious fruit, so when spring came that year and she saw the tree in blossom she was very excited and began to wonder what she might wish for.

When the apples were ready, Pomona picked one and took a bite. It was delicious! Her parents asked what she had wished for, and she told them that she could not think of anything she wanted. Her parents were happy to hear this. They explained to Pomona that their wish ten years ago was that they should have a daughter who would be so content that she should wish for nothing more than she had. Their wish had come true!

The Magic Cloak

There was once a woman who had a magic cloak. Whenever she wore it, people would believe every word she spoke, whether it was the truth or not. She used the magic cloak to make people do whatever she wanted them to.

She told one poor farmer that his grain was not worth more than a penny a sack, and so she bought her grain cheaply and the farmer grew poorer.

This wicked woman had a servant who found out about the magic cloak and was very annoyed with her for treating people this way. The servant, who was extremely clever, came up with a plan: she turned the magic cloak **inside out!** Her mistress put on the cloak and went off to cause some mischief. But when the woman spoke, she found she could only speak the **truth.**

When talking again to the farmer, she told him that his grain was the finest in the county and she should pay one hundred times more than she had.

As word of her behaviour went around the village, all those she had wronged came to see her and she could not help but tell them the truth. All her wrongs were put right. The woman was very puzzled and never wore the cloak again.

One, Two, Buckle my Shoe

One, two, buckle my shoe;

Three, four, knock at the door;

Five, six, pick up sticks;

Seven, eight, lay them straight;

Nine, ten, a big fat hen;

Eleven, twelve, dig and delve;

Thirteen, fourteen, maids a-courting;

Fifteen, sixteen, maids in the kitchen;

Seventeen, eighteen, maids in waiting;

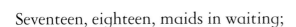

Nineteen, twenty, my plate's empty!

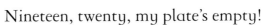

Our Home is a Castle!

Some people live in bungalows,
Without stairs to climb.
And some live way up in the clouds –
That must be sublime!

A man we know lives in a boat
And sails to where he pleases.
You can build a house with ice,
If all around you freezes!

But no one else has got a home
As wonderful as ours –
We live in a castle with a
Turret and some towers!

We can eat delicious food
In our banquet hall.
And when we're in a party mood,
We host a fancy ball!

The Washing Line!

My clothes are hanging on the line
So colourful and free,
They look like party bunting –
Hung up for all to see!

Red, blue, pink, yellow and green,
The colours are so bright,
They might be birds of paradise
Ready to take flight.

Some people don't like washing,
They look at me and ask:
How can you be so jolly about
Such a loathsome task?

To some it may seem like a chore
To wash and scrub and clean,
But I like nothing better than
My washing daydreams!

Visiting a Friend!

I'm going on a visit, to see my best friend, Grace.
She lives across the meadow in a very pretty place.
She hasn't got a ceiling, four walls or a door,
In fact she doesn't really even have a proper floor!

On my way I'll gather pretty flowers that I see,
To give to my friend Grace when I visit her for tea.
It's not an ordinary tea; she doesn't like cream cake,
She really much prefers to eat the flowers that I take!

She lives out in the open, beneath the sky, so blue.
She has four legs and a tail – have you figured out my clue?
Grace is not a human friend. She doesn't go to school.
Well of course she doesn't – ponies *don't* go, as a rule!

Yawning!

The strangest, funny feeling is creeping over me;
It makes me feel all stretchy, whatever can it be?
It's rising through my body; I cannot keep it in,
My arms are stretching upwards and my mouth is opening…

Yawn… oh my goodness! Yawn… oh, how strange!
My mouth is like a cavern on a mountain range.
Yawn… I can't stop it! Yawn… there it goes!
And if I try to close my mouth it comes out through my nose!

Yawn… well I never! Yawn… oh my, oh me!
I'm making such a strange noise, like a foghorn out at sea!
Yawn… I think it's catching! Yawn… it's your turn now.
Is there a way to stop a yawn? I wish you'd tell me how!

Fingers and Toes

These are my fingers and these are my toes.
This is my head and this is my nose.
These are my ears, on my head at the side.
These are my eyes, I can open them wide.

This is my mouth and here are my teeth.
These are my knees and my feet are beneath.
I can wave my arms and wiggle my nose.
I can stretch my arms and touch my toes.

I can clap my hands together, and then. . .
It's time to start all over again!

My Dog, Blue

My dog, Blue, is soft to touch –
I love to cuddle him so much.
His ears droop down in a cute way,
His tail can wag as if to say:

Cuddle me!

My dog, Blue, is my best friend,
So please don't ask me if I'll lend
My dog to you, the answer's no –
I take him everywhere I go...

... and cuddle him!

When it's time to go to bed,
I snuggle up and rest my head.
I love to be alone with Blue,
I'm sure you know just what I do...

... I cuddle him!

Hazel Squirrel

Hazel Squirrel had the finest tail of all the animals that lived beside Looking-Glass Pond.

It was fluffier than Dilly Duck's tail… bushier than Harvey Rabbit's tail… and swooshier than everybody's!

Each morning Hazel groomed her tail and admired her reflection in the pond. "I really do have a beautiful tail!" she would say, smiling at herself in the silvery water.

Sometimes Hazel played with her friends, but it usually ended in tears.

"You splashed my lovely tail!" Hazel would shout crossly, when she played leap-frog with Webster.

"You're getting my tail dirty, Harvey!" she would moan

very grumpily, when they played digging.

Soon, Hazel stopped playing with her friends altogether. "I'm far too busy brushing my tail!" she said whenever they came to call. "Come back some other time."

One morning, Hazel was admiring her tail by the pond as usual. Suddenly, she had a funny thought. She couldn't remember the last time she had seen her friends.

Hazel looked at her reflection in the pond. Staring back was a strange face... a cross face... a grumpy face. It was Hazel's face! Hazel couldn't believe her eyes. "No wonder my friends don't visit any more," she cried. "I've forgotten how to smile!"

The next day Hazel called for her friends. They had such fun playing leap-frog and digging muddy holes that she forgot all about her tail. "From now on," she laughed, "the only time I'll look at my reflection is to practise smiling!"

I'm a Big Sister!

Ellie was Mummy's and Daddy's little girl. But one day Mummy went into hospital – and when she came back she had a new baby with her.

"Now you're a big sister!" Mummy told Ellie.

Everyone made a big fuss of the new baby.

"Baby's so little!" Auntie Molly said. "Isn't it lovely to be a big sister?"

"Yes," said Ellie. But she wasn't so sure. Sometimes she wished she could be little again, like Baby.

When Baby's nappy needed changing, Ellie asked Mummy, "Did I wear a nappy too?"

Mummy smiled. "Yes you did, Ellie. But now you're too grown-up for nappies. Big sisters wear underpants. Yours have flowers on them."

"And I can put them on myself," said Ellie.

"That's right," said Mummy. "But Baby still needs lots of help – not like you!"

"Can I help change Baby's nappy?" Ellie asked.

"Of course," said Mummy. "Thank you. Baby's very lucky to have a big sister who helps!"

But Ellie still thought it might be fun to be as little as Baby.

The next day, when Daddy got the baby's bottle ready, Ellie asked, "Did I have my dinner in a bottle too?"

Daddy smiled. "Yes, Ellie," he said. "But now you're too grown-up for a bottle. Big sisters eat sandwiches and drink milk from a cup."

"And I can eat sandwiches and drink milk all by myself!" said Ellie. "I don't need anyone to help me."

"Of course you can," said Daddy. "That's what big sisters do. But Baby still needs lots of help."

"Can I help feed the baby?" Ellie asked Daddy.

"I think Baby would like that very much," said Daddy. "Baby's so lucky to have such a helpful big sister!"

That night, Ellie watched Mummy put Baby to sleep.

"Did I sleep in a cot like Baby's?" she asked.

"Yes, Ellie, you did. But now you're too grown-up for a cot," said Mummy. "Big sisters sleep in big, cosy beds, just like yours."

Ellie looked at her bed. With its pretty quilt and a huge pile of cuddly toys, it really did look cosy.

"There are no animals in Baby's cot," Ellie said. "Let's give Baby my yellow bunny – just for now."

"That's very kind of you, Ellie," said Mummy. "Baby is lucky to have a big sister who shares!"

The next day, Ellie and Mummy went out to the park. Baby came too, in a pushchair.

"Did I ride in a pushchair like Baby?" Ellie asked.

"Yes, you did," replied Mummy. "But you're a big sister now. Big sisters can walk – and run and jump. Baby can't do any of those things yet. Baby's lucky to have a strong, big sister like you!"

At the park, Ellie saw the ice cream van.

"Will you buy an ice cream for Baby?" she asked Mummy.

"No, Ellie," said Mummy. "Baby's too little for ice cream. But her big sister isn't! What flavour would you like?"

"Chocolate!" said Ellie. "Thank you!"

Ellie looked at Baby, and Baby smiled at her.

Ellie smiled too.

"I'm glad we have a baby," she told Mummy. "I get to help, and share and push the pushchair – and I get to have ice cream too! Being a big sister is the best!"

Nibbling Neighbours

One sunny morning in the meadow, Alice was happily munching away when she was surprised to discover a hole where there should be grass.

"My dears," she mooed, "there's a hole in our field!"

The next morning, where there had been one hole before, now there were five!

"If this goes on," said Bryony, "we'll have nowhere to stand!"

"And nothing to eat," added Rowan, sounding alarmed.

By the end of the week, there were over a hundred holes.

"You've got some nibbling neighbours," said Farmer Jim. "It looks like a family of rabbits has come to stay."

The cows shuddered. "Those hopping things with long ears?" asked Holly. "I can't look my best with them around!"

"And they have very, very large families," warned Rowan. "Not just one baby at a time, like cows do."

"It's odd we've never seen one," said Bryony thoughtfully. "I'm going to keep watch tonight."

That night, as the full moon rose over the meadow, Bryony pretended to go to sleep.

Although she was expecting it, she was shocked when two bright eyes and a twitchy nose popped up in front of her.

"*Aaaaaghh!*" cried Bryony.

"*Aaaaaghh!*" cried the rabbit, and disappeared down its hole.

"You should have followed it!" cried Alice, who had been woken by the sudden noise.

"Down a rabbit hole?" gasped Rowan. "Don't be silly, Alice. She's far too big!"

"Then we're doomed," said Holly, gloomily. "Those rabbits will take over without us even seeing them do it."

The next morning, the cows awoke to an amazing sight. Hundreds of rabbits were sitting around them.

"Excuse me!" said the largest one. "We've come to ask for your help."

"Help?" echoed Alice. "We're the ones who need help!"

The rabbit explained that his family lived in fear. "Your hoofs are so big, you could stamp on us without noticing."

Just then, Bryony had one of her excellent ideas. "You would be much safer," she said, "if you lived under the hedgerow."

So they did. All day in the meadow, there's munching and mooing. All night in the hedgerow, there's nibbling, digging and wiggling. And everyone is happy.

Birthday Sleepover

It was Ali's birthday and she had invited her friends to a special sleepover. As it was a warm summer evening, they were going to camp in the garden in Ali's new tent. They had been looking forward to it for weeks and were planning a special midnight feast.

The moon was shining brightly as the girls settled into the tent. Ali, Martha and Daisy zipped up the door and climbed into their sleeping bags.

"It's such a pity Ashley couldn't come," said Martha. "This is going to be so much fun!"

They unpacked their feast of crisps, biscuits and chocolate-spread sandwiches. As they tucked in, they made each other laugh with spooky ghost stories.

Daisy began telling them about an old barn nearby. Her brother had said it was haunted.

Then there was a bang from outside the tent.

"What was that?" asked Martha, looking worried.

"Just a cat, or something," said Ali, nervously.

They all listened again. There was another bang and then a noise that sounded like a twig snapping. Martha jumped. "That wasn't a cat!" she said, grabbing her torch.

"What's that strange rustling noise?" said Daisy.

Ali reached for her shoes. "I don't like this one bit!" she said.

"Let's get out of here!" yelled Daisy.

The girls grabbed their things and squeezed out of the tent.

"Quick! Follow me!" shouted Ali. She began to lead them across the grass towards the summerhouse.

"Wait!" said a voice behind them. "Where are you all going?" It was Ashley!

"My mum said I could come after all!" Ashley laughed. "But it was hard to find your tent in the dark."

Ali, Daisy and Martha laughed. "So it was you making all those noises!" said Daisy. "Not a ghost at all!"

Ali hugged Ashley. "I'm so glad you're here," she said. "It wouldn't have been a proper birthday without you."

"Now let's finish off this midnight feast!" cried Martha.

The Owl and the Pussy Cat

The Owl and the Pussy Cat went to sea
In a beautiful pea-green boat,
They took some honey, and plenty of money,
Wrapped up in a five pound note.
The Owl looked up to the stars above,
And sang to a small guitar,
"Oh lovely Pussy! Oh Pussy, my love,
What a beautiful Pussy you are, you are, you are,
What a beautiful Pussy you are."

Pussy said to the Owl, "You elegant fowl,
How charmingly sweet you sing.
Oh let us be married, too long we have tarried;
But what shall we do for a ring?"
They sailed away, for a year and a day,
To the land where the Bong-tree grows,
And there in a wood a piggy-wig stood
With a ring at the end of his nose, his nose, his nose,
With a ring at the end of his nose.

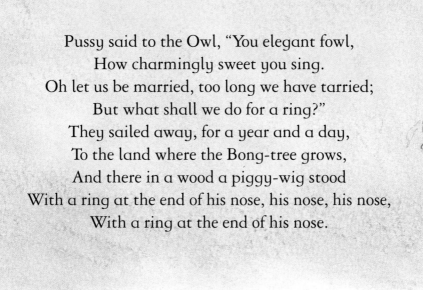

Wee Willie Winkie

Wee Willie Winkie
Runs through the town,
Upstairs and downstairs
In his nightgown.

Rapping at the window,
Crying through the lock,
Are all the children in their beds?
For now it's eight o'clock.

Boys and Girls Come Out to Play

Boys and girls come out to play,
The moon doth shine as bright as day!
Leave your supper and leave your sleep,
And join your playfellows in the street.
Come with a whoop and come with a call,
Come with a good will or not at all.

Five Little Monkeys

Five little monkeys jumping on the bed,
One fell off and bumped his head.
Mummy called the Doctor and the Doctor said,
"No more monkeys jumping on the bed!"

Four little monkeys jumping on the bed,
One fell off and bumped her head.
Mummy called the Doctor and the Doctor said,
"No more monkeys jumping on the bed!"

Three little monkeys jumping on the bed,
One fell off and bumped his head.
Mummy called the Doctor and the Doctor said,
"No more monkeys jumping on the bed!"

Two little monkeys jumping on the bed,
One fell off and bumped her head.
Mummy called the Doctor and the Doctor said,
"No more monkeys jumping on the bed!"

One little monkey jumping on the bed,
He fell off and bumped his head.
Mummy called the Doctor and the Doctor said,
"Put those monkeys straight to bed!"

A Special Day at Fairy School

It was Woodland Day in Fairyland, a special day when the fairies use their magic especially to help the woodland creatures. All the pupils at Fairy School were very excited because this year they were allowed to join in by practising their helpful spells. Isabella and Chloe, the youngest fairies of all, had been looking forward to this day for weeks.

Now the big day had arrived and all the fairies were busy helping. Aiden used his **magic** to help a spider mend her broken web. Holly helped a bee to find some nectar to drink. Their teacher, Mrs Spritely, was very pleased.

But Isabella and Chloe were sad because they couldn't make their magic work. They had tried to help a caterpillar turn into a butterfly but nothing had happened.

"Good try," said Mrs Spritely.

Chloe and Isabella **sighed** so deeply as they flew past a tree, that two little birds popped their heads out of their nest.

"Tweet! Tweet! Why are you both so sad?"

"We wanted to practise our magic, but we can't find anyone who needs our help," said Isabella.

"You can help us!" chirped the happy little chicks. They explained that they hadn't learned to fly yet and that they wanted to leave their nest and join in with all the fun of Woodland Day. Isabella and Chloe waved their magic wands over the two birds who instantly began to rise from their nest.

"Now flap your wings," cried Chloe. The spell had worked! Isabella and Chloe flew around the treetops with their fluffy new friends.

"Excellent work!" said Mrs Spritely, as Isabella and Chloe glowed with pride. They both decided that this had been the best Woodland Day ever!

Little Red Riding Hood

Once there was a little girl who always wore a red cape and hood. Everyone called her Little Red Riding Hood.

"Your granny isn't feeling well today," said Little Red Riding Hood's mother one morning. "Take this basket of food to her, but stay on the path and **don't** talk to any strangers on the way."

So Little Red Riding Hood skipped off into the woods to visit her granny. On the way, she noticed some pretty blue flowers growing just a little way off the path. "I'll just pick a few for Granny and then I'll be on my way," she thought.

But Little Red Riding Hood was not alone.

"Hello, little girl," said a deep **growling** voice. Little Red Riding Hood looked up and saw a wolf.

"Where are you off to?" asked the wolf.

"I'm going to visit my granny," replied Little Red Riding Hood,

who had already forgotten her mother's warning.

As Little Red Riding Hood continued along the path, the wolf ran as fast as he could to her granny's house. When he got there, he ate the granny in one big **gulp!** Then he disguised himself as the granny, climbed into bed and waited.

Soon, Little Red Riding Hood arrived.

"Granny, what big **eyes** you have," she said.

"All the better to see you with," replied the wolf.

"What big **ears** you have," went on the little girl.

"All the better to hear you with," replied the wicked wolf.

"And what big **teeth** you have," she said.

"All the better to eat you with!" said the wolf, and he swallowed her in one **gulp!** Then the wolf fell soundly asleep.

Luckily, a woodcutter was passing the cottage and heard the wolf's loud **snores.** He went into the cottage, grabbed the wolf and turned him upside down. Then he shook him and shook him until... out fell Little Red Riding Hood and her granny! The woodcutter, Little Red Riding Hood and her granny chased the wolf away. And he was never seen again.

The Amethyst Brooch

Of all the treasures in the world, Ella liked her grandmother's amethyst brooch the best. It was a beautiful purple colour and glinted in the light when she held it up to the window. Every time she went to visit her granny, she would ask to see the special brooch, and was sometimes even allowed to wear it for a little while, which was the best treat ever.

"Tell me how you got the brooch," Ella asked one day when she was visiting. "Did Grandpa give it to you?"

Ella's granny beckoned her over to where she was sitting and Ella knew that she was about to hear a story.

"A very long time ago," began Ella's grandmother, "when I was just a young girl, I worked in a big house for a family. I cleaned the house for them and looked after the young children. I grew very fond of the family and they grew fond of me, and so I stayed there for many years. The lady of the house had a beautiful purple brooch and I used to admire it when I helped her dress for a party.

"One day, a chauffeur came to the house to drive a shiny new car for the family. He was so handsome in his uniform that I fell in love with him straight away. That man was your grandfather. Luckily he felt the same way and he asked me to marry him.

"On the evening before my wedding day,
I was putting on my shawl ready to leave
when I noticed something glinting – it was
the beautiful **amethyst brooch!**
The lady I worked for had pinned it onto
my shawl as a surprise, because she
knew how much I liked it. And I have
treasured it ever since."

Brrrring! The doorbell rang
and broke the spell of the story. Ella
ran to answer the door. She knew it
would be her mother because today
was Ella's birthday and they were
going home to have a birthday
party. She ran to kiss her
granny goodbye and thought
she noticed a special **gleam** in
her eyes.

As Ella put her coat on ready to
leave, she noticed a **glint** of something
purple on the collar, and realised that it was her grandmother's
amethyst brooch!

"Happy birthday, Ella!" called her granny. "The
brooch is yours now."

"Thank you, Granny!" said Ella. "I will treasure it
forever!"

And she did.

The Timid Dragon

There was once a village that lived in fear of a dragon.

One day, a little girl called Rosa went out looking for wild flowers. She strayed off the path and found the **prettiest** flowers she had ever seen. As she began to pick them, she lost her footing and slid a little way down the mountain, twisting her ankle. She couldn't get up again, and so she began to cry.

She looked up and was terrified to see a fiery dragon's snout peeping out from behind a rock. Rosa **screamed,** the snout disappeared and Rosa began to cry louder. After a little while, she heard a soft gravelly sound and realised that it was the dragon singing. His song was so soothing that she felt less afraid. Soon the dragon peeped out again.

"Is it safe to come out now?" he asked.

"You won't eat me, will you?" asked Rosa.

"I was **worried** that you might hurt me," whispered the timid dragon. "Climb on my back and I'll fly you home."

When they arrived home, the villagers were scared, but Rosa told the dragon to sing his soothing song again. Soon everyone realised they had nothing to fear from him.

The villagers and the dragon lived together happily ever after.

The Princess Twins

Once upon a time, there were two pretty princess twins named Violet and Rose. They were identical. They each wore a ribbon in their hair; one **violet** and one **pink,** so that everyone knew which princess was which.

One day the princesses were feeling mischievous and decided to play a **trick** on their mother. Rosa put a violet ribbon in her hair so that now both twins looked like Violet. The two cheeky princesses put an empty picture frame in the garden.

"Mother," called Violet, "come and see our new mirror!"

The queen came out into the garden and saw Violet dancing in front of the mirror, and her reflection dancing back.

"What a **wonderful** mirror!" exclaimed the queen, as she went to see her own reflection.

But when she looked into the mirror, she was amazed to find she had no reflection.

The queen was puzzled... until she heard Rosa **giggling** from her hiding place behind a tree. Rosa, wearing her violet ribbon, had copied all of Violet's movements, and the queen had been fooled into believing that the empty frame was a mirror!

Anna Maria

Anna Maria she sat on the fire;
The fire was too hot, she sat on the pot;
The pot was too round, she sat on the ground;
The ground was too flat, she sat on the cat;
The cat ran away with Maria on her back.

Round-eared Cap

A pretty little girl in a round-eared cap
I met in the streets the other day;
She gave me such a thump,
That my heart it went bump;
I thought I should have fainted away!
I thought I should have fainted away!

Goldy Locks, Goldy Locks

Goldy locks, goldy locks,
Wilt thou be mine?
Thou shall not wash dishes,
Nor yet feed the swine;

But sit on a cushion,
And sew a fine seam,
And feed upon strawberries,
Sugar and cream.

Here We Go Round the Mulberry Bush

Here we go round the mulberry bush,
The mulberry bush, the mulberry bush,
Here we go round the mulberry bush,
On a cold and frosty morning.

This is the way we wash our hands,
Wash our hands, wash our hands,
This is the way we wash our hands,
On a cold and frosty morning.

This is the way we wash our clothes,
Wash our clothes, wash our clothes,
This is the way we wash our clothes,
On a cold and frosty morning.

Here we go round the mulberry bush,
The mulberry bush, the mulberry bush,
Here we go round the mulberry bush,
On a cold and frosty morning.

There Was an Old Man from Peru

There was an old man from Peru
Who dreamed he was eating his shoe.
He woke in a fright
In the middle of the night
And found it was perfectly true.

I Eat My Peas with Honey

I eat my peas with honey,
I've done it all my life,
It makes the peas taste funny,
But it keeps them on my knife.

Haymaking

The maids in the meadow
Are making the hay,
The ducks in the river
Are swimming away.

The Old Woman's Three Cows

There was an old woman who had three cows,
Rosy and Colin and Dun.
Rosy and Colin were sold at the fair,
And Dun broke her heart in a fit of despair.
So there was an end of her three cows,
Rosy and Colin and Dun.

Sing, Sing

Sing, sing,
What shall I sing?
The cat's run away
With the pudding string!
Do, do,
What shall I do?
The cat's run away
With the pudding too!

To the Snail

Snail, snail, put out
your horns,
And I will give you bread
and barley corns.

The Wheels on the Bus

The wheels on the bus go
Round and round,
Round and round,
Round and round.
The wheels on the bus go
Round and round,
All day long.

The wipers on the bus go
Swish, swish, swish!
Swish, swish, swish!
Swish, swish, swish!
The wipers on the bus go
Swish, swish, swish!
All day long.

The horn on the bus goes
Beep, beep, beep!
Beep, beep, beep!
Beep, beep, beep!
The horn on the bus goes
Beep, beep, beep!
All day long.

Roses are Red

Roses are red,
Violets are blue,
Sugar is sweet
And so are you.

Little Poll Parrot

Little Poll Parrot
Sat in his garret
Eating toast and tea;
A little brown mouse
Jumped into the house,
And stole it all away.

I Had a Little Horse

I had a little horse,
His name was Dappled Grey,
His head was made of gingerbread,
His tail was made of hay.
He could amble, he could trot,
He could carry the mustard pot,
He could amble, he could trot,
Through the old town of Windsor.

The Legacy

My father died a month ago
And left me all his riches;
A feather bed, a wooden leg,
And a pair of leather breeches;
A coffee pot without a spout,
And a cup without a handle,
A tobacco pipe without a lid,
And half a farthing candle.

Sowing Corn

One for the mouse
One for the crow,
One to rot,
One to grow.

Small Is the Wren

Small is the wren,
Black is the rook,
Great is the sinner
That steals this book.

Ariel's Song

Full fathom five thy father lies;
Of his bones are coral made;
Those are pearls that were his eyes:
Nothing of him that doth fade,
But doth suffer a sea-change
Into something rich and strange:
Sea nymphs hourly ring his knell.
Ding-dong!
Hark! now I hear them,
Ding-dong, bell!

A Frog He Would a-Wooing Go

A frog he would a-wooing go,
Heigho! says Rowley,
Whether his mother would let him or no,
With a rowley, powley, gammon and spinach.

A Candle

Little Nancy Etticoat
In a white petticoat,
And a red rose.
The longer she stands
The shorter she grows.

A Tisket, a Tasket

A tisket, a tasket,
A green and yellow basket.
I wrote a letter to my love,
And on the way I dropped it.
I dropped it, I dropped it,
And on the way I dropped it.
A little girl picked it up
And put it in her pocket.

My Black Hen

Tiggy-tiggy-touchwood, my black hen,
She lays eggs for gentlemen.
Sometimes nine and sometimes ten,
Tiggy-tiggy-touchwood, my black hen.

I Had a Little Hen

I had a little hen, the prettiest ever seen,
She washed me the dishes, and kept the house clean;
She went to the mill to fetch me some flour,
She brought it home in less than an hour;
She baked me my bread, she brewed me my ale,
She sat by the fire and told many a fine tale.

An Angel of My Own

Lizzie was a pretty little girl who lived with her mum, her dad and her baby brother Matthew.

Lizzie looked as good and sweet as a little angel, but she didn't always act like one. Sometimes, she could be very naughty indeed.

One afternoon, Lizzie's grandma came for tea. Grandma was very pleased to see Lizzie and baby Matthew.

"Lizzie, please kiss your grandma hello," said Mum. But Lizzie ran away from Grandma into the garden.

Later that evening, Lizzie wanted to play.

"Please play quietly, Lizzie," Mum said. "Matthew is asleep."

But Lizzie started jumping loudly across the floor.

Stamp! Stamp! Stamp! went Lizzie's feet. Matthew woke up and began to cry.

"Stop crying, Matthew," ordered Lizzie. She pulled a face

at him. Matthew cried even harder.

"Please be nice to Matthew," Mum said, when she saw what Lizzie was doing. Lizzie stuck out her tongue rudely.

That night, Lizzie felt unhappy. She thought about all the naughty things she'd done. She wished she could make everything all right.

In the middle of the night, Lizzie was sleeping peacefully.

Suddenly, a strange glow filled the room. Lizzie opened her eyes and next to her bed was a beautiful angel. The angel had a kind face and wonderful, shimmering wings.

"Hello, Lizzie," smiled the angel. "Don't be afraid. I know that you're feeling a bit sad. I've come to try and help you."

The angel took Lizzie by the hand. "Let's talk about all the things that have happened today, and think about how we could have made them better. It would make your grandma so happy if you would spend time with her."

"I didn't mean to run away from Grandma," said Lizzie.

"And what about baby Matthew?" asked the angel. "If you accidentally wake him up, why don't you try and make him laugh instead of cry?"

Lizzie nodded her head happily. That was a good idea. Lizzie felt much better.

The angel tucked Lizzie back into bed and stroked her face tenderly.

"I wish I could be a beautiful angel like you one day," Lizzie whispered.

The angel smiled. "Well Lizzie, you have to be very good to become an angel," she replied. "But I'm sure you can do it if you try."

Lizzie nodded her head. "Yes, I think I can," she said. "I'll be much nicer from now on."

The next afternoon, Lizzie's grandma came to tea. Without being asked, Lizzie ran up to her and gave her a big kiss.

"Hello, Lizzie!" said Grandma happily. "It's lovely to see you."

Lizzie and Grandma had a wonderful time. Lizzie drew Grandma a special picture, which she was very pleased with. Then they played lots of nice games together.

At teatime, everyone enjoyed all the lovely food Lizzie's mum had made.

That evening, after Grandma had
gone home, Lizzie wanted to play.

"Please play quietly," said
Mum. "Matthew's sleeping."

Lizzie had wanted to play
noisily. She started to jump
across the floor, but then
remembered what the angel
had said.

Matthew hadn't woken up,
so Lizzie tiptoed silently across
the room and chose a book from the
shelf. She sat quietly on a bean bag to
look at it.

Lizzie didn't make a single sound.

As the days and weeks passed by, Lizzie was hardly
naughty at all.

One day, Mum and Dad had a special surprise for her.

"We're very proud of you," said Dad, giving Lizzie a big
hug. "You've been such a good girl lately, we've got you
a present."

Dad handed Lizzie a box. Inside was a beautiful silver
necklace. There was an angel charm hanging from it.

"A little angel for our little angel," said Mum. She put the
necklace around Lizzie's neck.

"Oh! Thank you, Mum!" beamed Lizzie as she gave her
mum a great big hug.

Mina's Lucky Shoes

Mina loved ballet. She went to the Starlight Ballet School. She had a ballet class every week.

Mina loved her ballet teacher, Miss Silver.

"You dance very well, Mina," said Miss Silver.

Mina was very happy – except for one thing. She found one of the dance steps very hard! When Mina had to spin around very fast it made her dizzy. Sometimes she even fell over!

"Try again, Mina," said Miss Silver. "Keep your head in one place as you are spinning, and then turn it round quickly at the last minute. You will do it."

Mina tried again, but she just couldn't get the hang of it. Spinning still made her dizzy.

"I'll never be able to spin," she said sadly to her mum.

"I have an idea," said Mum. She went up to the attic. When she came back down again she was holding an old box.

She gave the box to Mina. There were some yellow ballet shoes inside. They were made of the most beautiful satin, but they were very old.

"Wow!" said Mina. "Whose are these?"

"These were my lucky ballet shoes when I was your age," said her mum.

Mina put on the yellow ballet shoes. They fitted perfectly.

Then she tried a spin. She thought hard about what Miss Silver had told her. She turned her head at the last minute. And Mina didn't feel dizzy!

"They are lucky!" she said to Mum.

Mum laughed. "Maybe they are," she said. "That's what I used to think. But maybe you've just learnt how to spin."

"They are definitely lucky," said Mina.

Mina wore the yellow ballet shoes for her next class. Her spinning was perfect.

"Well done, Mina," said Miss Silver, when she saw Mina spinning around the dance studio.

Mina was delighted!

Perfect Pony

Pepper thought that he was the luckiest pony on the whole of Merrymead Farm. He wasn't the most handsome, the smartest or even the fastest pony but Pepper didn't mind one bit. He knew he was the luckiest pony on the farm because Lucy owned him.

Lucy was never cross or mean and always took Pepper for the nicest of rides. She ignored the other children and their ponies when they laughed at Pepper for knocking down the odd jump or for going slower than everyone else.

"They're just jealous," she'd whisper. "Because you're the best pony on the whole farm." And most of the time, Pepper managed to believe her. After all, Lucy was always right.

One summer evening, Lucy rushed out to the meadow with a piece of paper in her hand.

"Look, Pepper," she cried. "There's going to be a gymkhana tomorrow right here on Merrymead Farm! There are going to be games and jumping and even a showing class. I can't wait. I know that we're going to win lots of lovely rosettes."

As Lucy rushed off to spread the news, the other ponies in the meadow started to snicker.

"Oh dear!" laughed Bluey, the largest of the ponies. "I don't think you're built for jumping."

"Your legs are too short to go fast," said Swallow, the quickest pony on the farm.

"You're far too scruffy for showing," said Ebony, the sleek and vain show pony.

That night, Pepper lay awake worrying about the gymkhana. "The other ponies are right," he thought. "I'm no good for anything. I'm bound to let Lucy down at the gymkhana."

As these thoughts tumbled through his head, Pepper fell into a restless, dream-filled sleep. He dreamt that a beautiful white horse appeared before him. "I am the Great White Horse," she whispered. "I've come to help you."

Pepper blinked as she called, "Fly with me to see the best pony on Merrymead Farm."

Pepper felt his hoofs lift from the ground.

"*Whooaah*," he cried,

waggling his legs as he soared through the sky.

"Now look below you," said the Great White Horse.

Pepper looked down on a familiar scene. "It's the farm," he cried. "And look, Lucy and I are trotting past the geese."

"Yes, and look at all the other ponies," said the Great White Horse. "While you march past the geese without any fuss, they shake with fear or run away."

The Great White Horse reared up and tossed her flowing mane and the scene beneath them changed.

Pepper watched as the children got their ponies ready for a ride. He couldn't help smiling as he watched himself and Lucy rubbing noses. That was one of their favourite games.

Behind Lucy, Pepper could see Bluey putting back his ears and waving his back leg at his little boy.

"Ooh! That's not nice," gasped Pepper.

"Exactly," said the Great White Horse. "Pepper, you are brave, loyal and kind. You are the perfect pony for Lucy. Just be yourself tomorrow and everything will be all right!"

In the gymkhana the next day the first class was the jumping. Pepper set off at a steady trot. Slowly but surely he sailed clear over each jump.

"Nearly there," he thought, as he launched himself at the last jump. But his back hoof tapped the pole and it rattled to the ground. Pepper couldn't believe his bad luck. But Lucy was delighted, particularly when she was given a red rosette for coming fourth.

In the egg and spoon race, Pepper trotted so steadily that Lucy didn't drop her egg once. Lucy was over the moon when they were given a yellow rosette for coming third.

And they did even better in the pole-bending race, even though Pepper's round belly made it rather difficult to bend quickly round the poles.

"Well done," said the judge, as she awarded Pepper a beautiful blue rosette for coming second.

The final event of the day was the showing class.

"All the other ponies are smarter than me," thought Pepper. But as he trotted round, he remembered the words of the Great White Horse and began to relax. He was so busy enjoying himself that it took a few seconds to realize that the judge was saying something.

"And the winners are Pepper and Lucy," the judge said, pinning a green rosette to Pepper's bridle.

Lucy laughed in delight and rubbed noses with Pepper.

Pepper gasped. Then he looked up at the sky.

"Thank you, Great White Horse," he whispered.

Mousie

Mousie comes a-creeping, creeping.
Mousie comes a-peeping, peeping.
Mousie says, "I'd like to stay, but I haven't time today."
Mousie pops into his hole
And says, "*Achoo!* I've caught a cold!"

Mrs Mason's Basin

Mrs Mason bought a basin,
Mrs Tyson said, "What a nice one,"
"What did it cost?" asked Mrs Frost,
"Half a crown," said Mrs Brown,
"Did it indeed," said Mrs Reed,
"It did for certain," said Mrs Burton.
Then Mrs Nix, up to her tricks,
Threw the basin on the bricks.

Flying High

Flying high, swooping low,
Loop-the-loop and round they go.
Catching currents, soaring fast,
Feathered friends come sweeping past.

Grandma's Glasses

These are Grandma's glasses,
This is Grandma's hat;
Grandma claps her hands like this,
And rests them in her lap.

These are Grandpa's glasses,
This is Grandpa's hat;
Grandpa folds his arms like this,
And has a little nap.

Tickly, Tickly

Tickly, tickly, on your knee,
If you laugh, you don't love me.

Build a House with Five Bricks

Build a house with five bricks,
One, two, three, four, five.
Put a roof on top,
And a chimney too,
Where the wind blows through!

Two Little Kittens

Two little kittens, one stormy night,
Began to quarrel, and then to fight;
One had a mouse, the other had none,
And that's the way the quarrel began.

"I'll have that mouse," said the biggest cat;
"You'll have that mouse? We'll see about that!"
"I will have that mouse," said the eldest son;
"You shan't have the mouse," said the little one.

I told you before 'twas a stormy night
When these two little kittens began to fight.
The old woman seized her sweeping broom,
And swept the kittens right out of the room.

The ground was covered with frost and snow,
And the two little kittens had nowhere to go.
So they laid them down on the mat at the door,
While the old woman finished sweeping the floor.

Then they crept in, as quiet as mice,
All wet with snow, and cold as ice,
For they found it was better, that stormy night,
To lie down and sleep than to quarrel and fight.

Princess Sleepyhead

Goodnight, Princess Sleepyhead!
It's time to climb the stairs to bed.
Tidy up. There's lots of mess!
Neatly hang your pretty dress.

Brush your teeth. Make sure they're clean.
Brush up and down until they gleam!
Put your jewels in their box.
Brush your long and silky locks.

Snuggle down, switch on your light.
It shines just like the stars at night.
Sleep tight beneath its cosy beams –
Goodnight, Princess. Have sweet dreams!

Gilly Silly Jarter

Gilly Silly Jarter,
Who has lost a garter,
In a shower of rain,
The miller found it,
The miller ground it,
And the miller gave it
To Silly again.

The Broom Song

Here's a large one for the lady,
Here's a small one for the baby;
Come buy, my pretty lady,
Come buy o' me a broom.

Cock Crow

The cock's on the wood pile
Blowing his horn,
The bull's in the barn
A-threshing the corn.

Chairs to Mend

If I'd as much money as I could spend,
I never would cry, "Old chairs to mend.
Old chairs to mend! Old chairs to mend!"
I never would cry, "Old chairs to mend!"

Puss in the Pantry

Hie, hie, says Anthony,
Puss is in the pantry,
Gnawing, gnawing,
A mutton, mutton bone;
See how she tumbles it,
See how she mumbles it,
See how she tosses
The mutton, mutton bone.

My Maid Mary

My maid Mary,
She minds the dairy,
While I go a-hoeing and mowing each morn;
Merrily runs the reel,
And the little spinning wheel,
Whilst I am singing and mowing my corn.

The Gossips

Miss One, Two, and Three
Could never agree,
While they gossiped around
A tea-caddy.

Engine, Engine

Engine, engine, number nine,
Sliding down Chicago line;
When she's polished she will shine,
Engine, engine, number nine.

Buff

I had a dog
Whose name was Buff,
I sent him for
A bag of snuff;
He broke the bag
And spilt the stuff,
And that was all
My penny's worth.

Puss at the Door

Who's that ringing at my doorbell?
A little pussycat that isn't very well.
Rub its little nose with a little mutton fat,
That's the best cure for a little pussycat.

Three Ghostesses

Three little ghostesses,
Sitting on postesses,
Eating buttered toastesses,
Greasing their fistesses,
Up to their wristesses.
Oh what beastesses
To make such feastesses!

Washing Day

The old woman must stand
At the tub, tub, tub,
The dirty clothes to rub, rub, rub;
But when they are clean,
And fit to be seen,
She'll dress like a lady
And dance on the green.

Beauty and the Beast

Once, a girl called Beauty lived with her father and sisters.

One day her father was going to town and he asked his daughters what they would like him to bring them.

"I want a new dress," said the first sister.

"I want a new hat," said the second sister.

"I would like a **red rose,**" said Beauty.

The father bought the dress and hat, but he couldn't find a red rose anywhere.

On the way back, he passed a beautiful garden where he could see a red rose growing, so he picked one.

Suddenly, there was a terrible roar and an ugly beast appeared. **"Why have you stolen my rose?"** he said.

"It's for my daughter."

"Take the rose," said the Beast. "But give me your daughter in return, or you will die."

The father went home and told his daughters about the ugly Beast.

"I will go to the Beast," said Beauty, bravely.

The Beast's castle was warm and there was good food to eat, so

Beauty was comfortable there, although she missed her family. Every evening the ugly Beast appeared. He was kind to Beauty, so she grew to like him very much.

One evening, the Beast gave Beauty a magic mirror. When she looked into it, she saw that her father was sick.

"I must go to my father," said Beauty.

"Promise you will come back to me," said the Beast.

Beauty went home to look after her father. He was soon better, but she forgot her promise to the Beast.

One day, Beauty looked in the magic mirror and saw that the Beast was sick. Then she remembered her promise.

"I must go back to the Beast," said Beauty, and she hurried back to the castle. The Beast lay beside the red rose bush.

"Please do not die, Beast," said Beauty. "I love you."

As if by magic, the Beast changed into a handsome prince.

"I was under a magic spell," said the prince. "But your loving words, spoken from the heart, broke the spell."

Soon after, Beauty and the prince were married, and they lived happily ever after.

Sleeping Beauty

Once upon a time, a king and queen had a beautiful baby girl.

"Let's have a party to celebrate," the king beamed.

"Oh, yes!" agreed the queen. "You send out the invitations, my dear. I am just so busy looking after the baby!"

The day of the party arrived. Tables were laden with delicious food and there was music and dancing in the great hall. One by one, the guests placed their presents beside the princess's cradle. Last of all, the four good fairies presented their gifts in a shower of fairy dust.

"You will be incredibly clever," said Whim.

"You will be a wonderful dancer," said Whirl.

"You will be a fabulous singer," said Whiny.

But before Wisp, the fourth good fairy could speak, there was a flash of lightning, followed by a wicked cackle. Ha! Ha! Ha!

A hush fell over the great hall. It was Wheedle, the wicked fairy. The king had forgotten to send her an invitation – and she was furious!

"Here's my gift," she shrieked. "One day, the princess will prick her finger on a spindle and **die.**" Then she disappeared in a puff of black smoke.

Everyone gasped. The queen sobbed and the king shouted for the guards to burn every spinning wheel and spindle in the land.

Then Wisp fluttered up. "I cannot break the spell," she said, "but I can change it. If the princess does prick her finger, she will not die. She will fall into a deep sleep and will one day be woken by a **kiss of true love.**"

The years passed and the princess grew up to be everything the good fairies had promised. Then one day, she was exploring the castle when she came across a secret door. It led to a tower she had never seen before. She climbed the steep staircase and entered a tiny room. There, in the corner, was a long-forgotten spinning wheel. The princess had never seen anything like it. She brushed off the cobwebs and pricked her finger. Instantly, she fell into a deep sleep, along with everyone else in the castle.

A hundred years rolled by and a giant hedge of thorns grew up around the castle. Many tried to cut their way through the thorns, but all failed. Then one day, a handsome prince came riding by. When he saw the tower poking up from the forest of thorns, he became very curious.

He drew out his sword to hack his way through but somehow a path **magically** appeared before him.

At last the prince came to the castle. He walked past the snoring guards at the gate and stopped to admire the smart horses dozing in the stables. He almost tripped over the cook slumped beside her cooking pot. He bowed before the king and queen sleeping on their thrones. Then, as if in a trance, he was drawn up the steps of the tower.

As soon as the prince set eyes upon the princess, his heart leapt. He had never seen anyone so lovely in his life. He bent down and kissed her gently on the lips.

The princess opened her eyes and smiled. "I've had such a lovely sleep," she sighed.

As she spoke the words, everyone in the castle woke up and went about their tasks as if nothing had happened. The guards stood to attention, the grooms continued brushing the horses and the cook stirred her cooking pot.

The king and the queen were delighted. Not only had the handsome prince broken the wicked spell, but he was in love with their beautiful daughter.

"Excellent!" bellowed the king. "Let's have a royal wedding!"

The prince and princess were soon married and the king threw a fabulous party. He invited everyone, apart from the wicked fairy. Luckily, this time the good fairies cast a spell to make sure she stayed away and everything ran smoothly.

After the wedding, the prince and princess rode off on the prince's fine horse and lived happily ever after.

Rumpelstiltskin

Once upon a time, there was a miller who had a daughter.

One day the king rode by. "My daughter can spin straw into gold," said the miller, who was **nervous** and told the king the first silly thing that came into his head.

But the king believed the foolish man and took his daughter away. He locked her in a room full of straw.

"Spin this straw into **gold**," said the king. But the miller's daughter could not spin straw into gold and began to cry.

After crying for some time, a strange little man appeared.

"I know how to spin straw into gold," he said. "What will you give me if I help you?"

"I will give you my necklace," said the miller's daughter.

The little man spun all the straw into gold and then left.

When the king saw the piles of gold, he was very pleased.

He then took the miller's daughter to an even **bigger** room, full of straw. "If you can spin this straw into gold, I will marry you," said the king.

Again the girl began to cry and the little man came back to see her.

"I need your help, but I have nothing to give you," she sobbed.

"I will help you again," said the little man, "but in return you must give me your first **baby**." The girl reluctantly agreed.

The straw was spun into huge piles of gold and the little man left.

The king kept his **promise** and married the miller's daughter and before long, a baby was born. But when the little man came to take the baby, the queen began to cry as if her heart would break.

"I will not take your baby if you can **guess** my name," said the man. "I will give you until the morning to guess it."

That night, the queen went for a walk in the woods and, by chance, saw the little man dancing round a fire singing,

"My name is Rumpelstiltskin. Rumpelstiltskin is my name."

In the morning, the little man came to see the queen.

"Is your name Don or Ron?" asked the queen.

"No! No!" said the little man.

"Is it Bill?" asked the queen.

"No! No!" said the man. Then the queen said, "Is your name Rumpelstiltskin?"

"Yes! Yes!" said the little man, and off he ran away, never to be seen again.

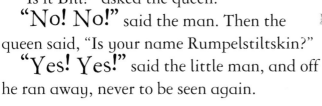

The Tomboy Princess

Princess Lily didn't like wearing dresses.

"Trousers are better," she insisted. "How am I supposed to climb trees in a big puffy dress?"

"Princesses are not supposed to climb trees," complained her parents.

But that didn't stop Lily. She loved playing outdoors and was always getting into the kind of scrapes that weren't expected of a princess.

"Young lady," warned her father one day, "it's about time you started acting less like a stable boy and more like a princess."

The king decided that he would throw a fancy ball for his daughter, and then she would have to wear a dress and be lady-like.

On the day of the ball, Princess Lily was fed up. It was a sunny day and she wanted to be outside riding her horse and looking for adventure, not cooped up indoors getting ready for a silly ball.

The royal hairdresser was called to do Lily's hair.

"Tut! Tut!" he mumbled as he tried to fashion Lily's scruffy locks into something more sophisticated.

When the queen arrived with a big puffy pink dress, Princess Lily had no choice but to put it on.

"I look so silly," she complained. "It's just not me!"

But the queen told her that she looked just perfect, and as she walked into the ballroom there was a hush as all the guests admired her – she looked so lovely!

Waiting to greet her was a handsome young prince.

"May I have the honour of this dance?" asked the prince.

"I suppose so," replied Princess Lily, rather rudely.

As they danced, the princess couldn't help sighing and the prince asked her what the matter was. When the princess explained that she would rather be outside in the fresh air, the young prince was delighted.

"I find these balls rather dull, too," he confessed. The prince and princess waited until nobody was looking and sneaked away into the garden. They climbed trees, ran in the fresh air and had a wonderful time.

"This is the best ball ever," said the prince happily, "but I wouldn't want to be in your shoes when your mother sees the state of your dress!"

The Vain Princess and her Servant

There was once a very vain princess who was always looking in the mirror. Her servant, however, was far prettier, although she didn't even own a mirror. The servant found pleasure in the nature around her, and her **happiness** made her very pretty.

The princess was to be married, and many princes came to meet her. At first, she was very excited. But none of the princes asked for her hand in marriage. The vain princess was so upset that she ran out into the garden where she heard a beautiful melody. She saw that it was her servant **singing** happily. The servant held an armful of wild flowers and her eyes shone brightly. She looked so pretty!

The princess joined her servant and soon forgot her cares. She began to enjoy what she saw around her, and she stopped looking in the mirror. As the princess grew happier, she became **prettier.** News of her beauty spread far and wide. Princes lined up to ask for her hand, but she was too busy enjoying the wonders of the world to think about marriage, and so they had to wait.

The Tree with the Golden Leaf

There was once a farmer who set off to cut down
an old chestnut tree that no longer bore fruit.
He was about to begin when he noticed that
the tree had one **glistening** golden leaf.
Thinking he was dreaming, he went to
a nearby brook and splashed his face to
wake himself up.

To his amazement, the brook spoke:
*"Wash out your eyes and look again
upon the chestnut tree. Although it bears no
fruit, behold its treasures a-plenty."*

The farmer took another careful
look at the old tree and noticed baby
birds, squirrels and insects. There were
so many things in the tree that he
hadn't noticed at first, but the golden
leaf he had seen was gone.

The farmer picked up his axe and
set off home. As he walked back
along the brook, he thought he heard
it talk to him again:

"All that glitters is not gold."

Can I See Another's Woe?

Can I see another's woe,
And not be in sorrow, too?
Can I see another's grief,
And not seek for kind relief?

Bob Robin

Little Bob Robin,
Where do you live?
Up in yonder wood, sir,
On a hazel twig.

Old Farmer Giles

Old Farmer Giles,
He went seven miles
With his faithful dog Old Rover;
And his faithful dog Old Rover,
When he came to the stiles,
Took a run, and jumped clean over.

Red Stockings

Red stockings, blue stockings,
Shoes tied up with silver;
A red rosette upon my breast
And a gold ring on my finger.

Fidget

As little Jenny Wren
Was sitting by the shed,
She waggled with her tail,
She nodded with her head;
She waggled with her tail,
She nodded with her head;
As Little Jenny Wren
Was sitting by the shed.

The Dove Says

The dove says, "Coo, coo! What shall I do?
I can scarce maintain two."
"Pooh, pooh," says the wren, "I have ten,
And keep them all like gentlemen.
Curr dhoo, curr dhoo! Love me and I'll love you!"

Dreams

Beyond, beyond the mountain line,
The grey-stone and the boulder,
Beyond the growth of dark green pine,
That crowns its western shoulder,
There lies that fairy land of mine,
Unseen of a beholder.

Its fruits are all like rubies rare,
Its streams are clear as glasses:
There golden castles hang in air,
And purple grapes in masses,
And noble knights and ladies fair
Come riding down the passes.

Ah me! They say if I could stand
Upon those mountain ledges,
I should but see on either hand
Plain fields and dusty hedges:
And yet I know my fairy land
Lies somewhere o'er their hedges.

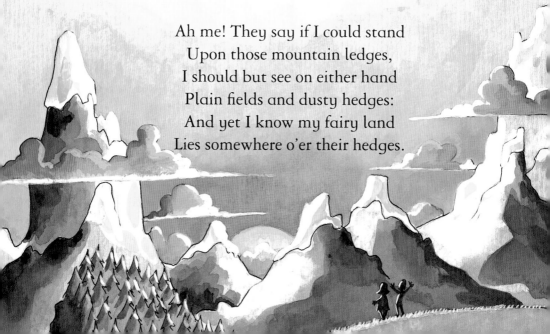

Three Little Kittens

Three little kittens,
They lost their mittens,
And they began to cry,
"Oh, mother dear,
We sadly fear
Our mittens we have lost."

"What? Lost your mittens,
You naughty kittens!
Then you shall have no pie.
Miaow, miaow, miaow, miaow.
No, you shall have no pie."

The three little kittens,
They found their mittens,
And they began to smile,
"Oh, mother dear,
See here, see here,
Our mittens we have found."

"What? Found your mittens,
You clever kittens!
Then you shall have some pie.
Purr, purr, purr, purr.
Oh, let us have some pie."

Fishes Swim

Fishes swim in water clear,
Birds fly up into the air,
Serpents creep along the ground,
Boys and girls run round and round.

Feathers

Cackle, cackle, Mother Goose,
Have you any feathers loose?
Truly have I, pretty fellow,
Half enough to fill a pillow.
Here are quills, take one or two,
And down to make a bed for you.

Cut Thistles

Cut thistles in May,
They'll grow in a day;
Cut them in June,
That is too soon;
Cut them in July,
Then they will die.

Pussycat and Robin

Little Robin Redbreast sat upon a tree,
Up went pussycat, and down went he!
Down came pussy, and away Robin ran;
Says little Robin Redbreast,
"Catch me if you can!"

Robin and Pussycat

Little Robin Redbreast jumped upon a wall,
Pussycat jumped after him,
And almost got a fall!
Little Robin chirped and sang,
And what did pussy say?
Pussycat said, "Mew,"
And Robin jumped away.

Three Blind Mice

Three blind mice, three blind mice!
See how they run, see how they run!
They all ran after the farmer's wife,
Who cut off their tails with a carving-knife,
Did ever you see such a thing in your life,
As three blind mice?

Oranges and Lemons

Oranges and lemons,
Say the bells of St Clements.
I owe you five farthings,
Say the bells of St Martins.
When will you pay me?
Say the bells of Old Bailey.
When I grow rich,
Say the bells of Shoreditch.

London Bells

Gay go up and gay go down,
To ring the bells of London town.
Halfpence and farthings,
Say the bells of St Martin's.
Pancakes and fritters,
Say the bells of St Peter's.
Two sticks and an apple,
Say the bells of Whitechapel.

My Little Cow

I had a little cow,
Hey diddle, ho diddle!
I had a little cow, and I drove it to the stall;
Hey diddle, ho diddle! And there's my song all.

Jemmy Dawson

Brave news is come to town,
Brave news is carried;
Brave news is come to town,
Jemmy Dawson's married.

I See the Moon

I see the moon,
And the moon sees me;
God bless the moon,
And God bless me.

For Every Evil Under the Sun

For every evil under the sun,
There is a remedy, or there is none.
If there be one, try and find it;
If there be none, never mind it.

My Best Friend

Emily was playing in the back garden with her favourite doll, Hannah.

"Hello, Emily!" called a cheerful voice.

It was Sarah, who lived next door. The two girls were best friends.

"Can I play with Hannah, too?" asked Sarah, reaching out to pick her up.

Emily held on tightly to Hannah. She was a very special doll, and Emily didn't like anybody else to play with her.

"Hannah's tired," said Emily. "I think I'll put her to bed. Then I'll come back and play with you."

For the rest of the morning, Emily and Sarah played in Emily's treehouse. It was their special hideout, and nobody else was allowed in it.

They both thought it was great living next door to one another.

The next day, both girls got up early and ran down to the front garden. They were very excited. They were going on holiday together. Every year, they went to the same holiday cottage. Sarah was travelling with Emily's family. That way they could talk to each other on the journey.

"Can Hannah sit between us?" Sarah asked Emily as they climbed into the car.

"Sorry," said Emily. "Hannah says she wants to sit by the window." And she tucked Hannah safely out of Sarah's reach.

At last they arrived at the cottage, and the girls raced from room to room checking that nothing had changed since last year. At bedtime, they snuggled down in their cosy beds in the attic. They loved sharing a room on holiday. They stayed awake long after the lights went out, talking and laughing together.

This holiday was the best one yet. One day Sarah rode her bicycle without stabilisers for the first time. The next day Emily did the same. Soon the girls were racing each other.

"Can we carry on racing each other when we get home?" Sarah asked her mum and dad. Her mum frowned.

"Hmmm," she began. "There's something we've been meaning to tell you. We're moving away. Daddy's got a new job, and we've found a wonderful new house."

Emily and Sarah couldn't believe their ears. They wouldn't be neighbours any more!

"It's not too far. You'll still be able to see Emily at weekends and during holidays," Dad said.

"But I don't want to move!" cried Sarah. She threw her arms around Emily. "You won't forget me, will you?" she whispered.

Back at home after the holiday, the last days of the summer flew by. On the morning that Sarah and her family were due to leave, Emily and her parents came outside to say goodbye.

"I've brought you a present to remember me by," said Sarah, handing Emily the gift. Emily ripped off the paper. Nestled inside was a gorgeous golden heart necklace.

"It's beautiful!" Emily smiled. Then she rushed inside her house. She came out a minute later carrying Hannah.

"Here," she said, putting the doll into Sarah's arms. "Hannah will keep you company until you make friends at your new house."

Sarah was speechless. She gave Emily an enormous hug.

Emily grinned. "Sharing really is great," she declared. "Especially sharing things with your very best friend."

The Case of the Ghost in the Attic

Molly was doing her homework with Carlos one evening when there was a knock at the front door. It was Mrs Dimley, the next-door neighbour. She looked a bit frightened.

"Is anything the matter?" asked Molly's mum.

"I think my house is haunted!" Mrs Dimley replied.

Molly grew excited. She loved ghost stories.

"At night, I can hear bumping coming from my attic," explained Mrs Dimley.

Molly's mum made everyone a nice cup of tea, and Mrs Dimley said she felt better.

But next evening Mrs Dimley came back looking upset. "My lights aren't working now, and the TV keeps going on and off," she said. "If this doesn't stop, I'll have to move house!"

Molly didn't want her to leave. It was time to investigate!

"Mum, can we borrow a torch?" she asked. "We're going next door to look in Mrs Dimley's attic."

"I'll come with

you," said her dad.

Molly's dad helped her and Carlos up into Mrs Dimley's attic. When Molly switched on her torch, she couldn't believe her eyes. What a mess! There were shredded newspapers everywhere. Hiding in a corner there was a family of frightened squirrels.

"Dad!" called Molly. "Look what we've found!"

Her dad climbed up the ladder and looked into the attic. "Those squirrels must have got in through that hole in the roof," he chuckled. "They've chewed through lots of wires. No wonder Mrs Dimley's electricity isn't working properly!"

Carlos ran next door to tell Mrs Dimley the news.

"Thank goodness for that!" she said. She phoned a vet, who came round straight away.

"I'll take your squirrels to the local park," he said.

"And I'll mend the hole in your roof," said Molly's dad.

Mrs Dimley was pleased. "You're all so kind," she said. She gave Molly and Carlos a big hug. "And you two are very clever kids!"

The Midnight Fairies

Megan was staying with Grandma for a few days, while Mum was away.

Megan always had fun at Grandma's. But on the second night of Megan's visit, as she was getting ready for bed, Megan realized that she'd lost the pretty flower necklace Mum had given her. Megan and Grandma looked everywhere, but they couldn't find it.

Grandma gave Megan a hug. "Don't worry. We'll look in the garden tomorrow," she promised. "I'm sure it will be there."

Megan settled down to sleep, but she tossed and turned and finally woke up again. She couldn't stop thinking about her lost necklace.

Getting out of bed, she went to look out of the window. Somewhere in the distance, a clock chimed once... twice... twelve times. "Midnight!" Megan thought. Suddenly her eyes opened wide. At the bottom of the moonlit garden, where the wild flowers grew, lights began to wink and twinkle, and shimmering shapes danced in the air.

Fairies had come out to play! They danced and skipped through the air, laughing and flitting from flower to flower.

All at once Fairy Firefly spotted something – a silver necklace gleaming in the grass.

"Look!" she said to her fairy friends.

"I wonder who this belongs to!"

"Maybe it's that little girl's," said Nightingale, pointing up to the window where Megan was looking out. "She looks very sad – as if she's lost something special."

"I wish we could make her smile again," said Moon Blossom.

The fairies looked at one another, and knew they were all thinking the same thing. First, they tucked the necklace safely behind a stone. Then, together, they flew across the garden and straight up to Megan's window.

As Megan gasped with amazement and delight, Stardust sprinkled her with glittering fairy dust.

"Now you'll be able to fly with us!" the fairies said happily.

With a fairy holding each hand, Megan whooshed out of the window and flew down to the bottom of the garden. When they landed, Stardust introduced herself and her friends. "We are the Midnight Fairies," she explained. "Every night at midnight, we come out to dance and play in the moonlight.

Will you be our friend and play with us tonight?"

"Of course I will!" said Megan happily.

With the moon beaming down and the friendly stars twinkling above, Megan and the fairies danced among the wild flowers. The cool grass tickled Megan's toes, and the fairies' laughter sounded like tiny crystal bells. Megan laughed with them, and felt happier than she ever had before.

When Megan was too tired to dance any more, Firefly said, "We have a surprise for you." She brought out Megan's necklace.

"My necklace!" cried Megan. "You found it! Thank you!"

As Firefly gave the necklace back, Stardust sprinkled magic fairy dust over it. A beautiful fairy appeared in place of the flower.

"Oh!" breathed Megan. "How wonderful. It's you! It's a Midnight Fairy!"

"Yes," said Firefly. "But please don't tell anyone how it got there, or we might lose our fairy magic."

"I promise!" replied Megan.

As she put on her

necklace, Megan realized that she could barely keep her eyes open. With the Midnight Fairies fluttering over her, she curled up under the oak tree and fell asleep... until the morning, when she woke up, tucked up in her cosy bed in Grandma's house!

"How did I get back here?" Megan wondered. "Was it just a dream?"

She reached up to her neck – and there was her necklace, right where it should be.

"Hello!" said Grandma cheerfully, opening the bedroom door.

"Grandma, look!" said Megan. "I have my necklace back! Did *you* find it?"

"No, dear," said Grandma, with a puzzled look. She peered down at the necklace. "Oh, how lovely!" she said. "I hadn't noticed the fairy before."

"The Midnight Fairies!" Megan thought to herself. "So it wasn't a dream, after all!"

"I wonder how your necklace got back here," said Grandma, scratching her head.

Megan, smiling as she looked out towards the garden, knew the answer. But it was a secret that belonged to her – to her and the Midnight Fairies, the wonderful, magical friends she would never, ever forget.

Rain, Rain, Go Away!

It was a rainy day and Raindrop the fairy liked the rain.

"Come and play outside," Raindrop said to the other fairies.

The other fairies did not like the rain. "It's too wet to play outside," they said.

All the fairies lived at the bottom of a garden that belonged to Ann and Tom.

Ann and Tom looked out of the window.

"I'm bored," said Ann.

"It's too wet to play outside," said Tom.

"I'm bored of being inside," said Ann.

Down at the bottom of the garden, Raindrop had started to cry because no one wanted to play with her. And the more Raindrop cried, the more it rained. Soon it was pouring!

Sunny the sunshine fairy looked at the rain. "Don't cry, Raindrop," she said. "I will play with you."

Raindrop stopped crying. Like magic, the rain stopped. The sun came out.

Ann and Tom came out to play in the garden.

"Look! A beautiful rainbow!" they said.

Like a Duck to Water

Mrs Duck swam proudly across the
farm pond followed by a line of fluffy
ducklings. Hidden in the safety of the
nest, Dozy Duckling peeked out and
watched them go. He wished he was
brave enough to go with them but
he was afraid of the water!

When they returned that night
they told him tales of all the scary
animals they had met by the pond.

"There's a big thing with hot breath called Horse," said Dotty.

"There's a huge smelly pink thing called Pig," said Dickie.

"But worst of all," said Doris, "there's a great grey bird
called Heron. He gobbles up little ducklings for breakfast!"

At that all the little ducklings squawked with fear and
excitement.

Next morning, Mrs Duck hurried the ducklings out for
their morning parade. Dozy kept his eyes shut until they had
gone, then looked up to see a great grey bird towering over
him! He leaped into the water crying, "Help, wait for
me!" But the others started laughing!

"It's a trick! Heron won't eat you. We just
wanted you to come swimming. And you've
taken to it like a duck to water!"

Twinkle, Twinkle

Twinkle, twinkle, little star,
How I wonder what you are!
Up above the world so high,
Like a diamond in the sky.

When the blazing sun is gone,
When he nothing shines upon,
Then you show your little light,
Twinkle, twinkle, all the night.

Then the traveller in the dark,
Thanks you for your tiny spark,
He could not see which way to go,
If you did not twinkle so.

As your bright and tiny spark,
Lights the traveller in the dark —
Though I know not what you are,
Twinkle, twinkle, little star.

Sleep, Baby, Sleep

Sleep, baby, sleep,
Your father keeps the sheep;
Your mother shakes the dreamland tree
And from it fall sweet dreams for thee;
Sleep, baby, sleep.

Sleep, baby, sleep,
The large stars are the sheep;
The little stars are the lambs, I guess,
And the gentle moon is the shepherdess;
Sleep, baby, sleep.

Sleep, baby, sleep,
Your father keeps the sheep;
Your mother guards the lambs this night,
And keeps them safe till morning light;
Sleep, baby, sleep.

Frère Jacques

Frère Jacques, Frère Jacques,
Dormez-vous, dormez-vous?
Sonnez les matines, sonnez les matines,
Ding, dang, dong, ding, dang, dong.

O Lady Moon

O Lady Moon, your horns point toward the east:
Shine, be increased.
O Lady Moon, your horns point toward the west:
Wane, be at rest.

Ding, Dong, Bell

Ding, dong, bell,
Pussy's in the well!
Who put her in?
Little Tommy Green.
Who pulled her out?
Little Johnny Stout.
What a naughty boy was that
To try to drown poor pussycat,
Who never did any harm,
But killed the mice in his father's barn.

Muffin Man

Have you seen the muffin man,
The muffin man, the muffin man,
Have you seen the muffin man
That lives in Drury Lane, O?

The Coachman

Up at Piccadilly, O!
The coachman takes his stand,
And when he meets a pretty girl,
He takes her by the hand;
Whip away for ever, O!
Drive away so clever, O!
All the way to Bristol, O!
He drives her four-in-hand.

The Miller of Dee

There was a jolly miller
Lived on the river Dee:
He worked and sang from morn till night,
No lark so blithe as he;
And this the burden of his song for ever used to be:
I jump me jerrime jee!
I care for nobody – no! not I,
Since nobody cares for me.

Star Light, Star Bright

Star light, star bright,
First star I see tonight,
I wish I may, I wish I might,
Have the wish I wish tonight.

Little Cottage

Little cottage in the wood,
Little old man by the window stood,
Saw a rabbit running by,
Knocking at the door.
"Help me! Help me! Help me!" he said,
"Before the huntsman shoots me dead."
"Come little rabbit, come inside,
Safe with me abide."

Here Is The Church

Here is the church,
Here is the steeple,
Open the doors,
And here are the people.
Here is the parson,
Going upstairs,
And here he is
A-saying his prayers.

How Many Miles to Babylon?

How many miles to Babylon? –
Threescore and ten.
Can I get there by candlelight? –
Aye, and back again!

A Swarm of Bees in May

A swarm of bees in May
Is worth a load of hay;
A swarm of bees in June
Is worth a silver spoon;
A swarm of bees in July
Is not worth a fly.

Tinker, Tailor

Tinker, tailor,
Soldier, sailor,
Rich man, poor man,
Beggarman, thief!

Ring-a-Ring o' Roses

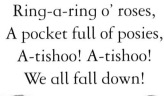

Ring-a-ring o' roses,
A pocket full of posies,
A-tishoo! A-tishoo!
We all fall down!

See A Pin and Pick It Up

See a pin and pick it up,
All the day you'll have good luck;
See a pin and let it lay,
Bad luck you'll have all the day!

Miss Mary Mack

Miss Mary Mack, Mack, Mack,
All dressed in black, black, black,
With silver buttons, buttons, buttons,
All down her back, back, back.
She went upstairs to make her bed,
She made a mistake and bumped her head;
She went downstairs to wash the dishes,
She made a mistake and washed her wishes;
She went outside to hang her clothes,
She made a mistake and hung her nose.

Nothing-at-all

There was an old woman called Nothing-at-all,
Who rejoiced in a dwelling exceedingly small;
A man stretched his mouth to its utmost extent,
And down at one gulp house and old woman went.

There Was an Old Woman Had Three Sons

There was an old woman had three sons,
Jerry and James and John:
Jerry was hung, James was drowned,
John was lost and never was found,
And there was an end of the three sons,
Jerry and James and John!

Old Mother Goose

Old Mother Goose,
When she wanted to wander,
Would ride through the air
On a very fine gander.

Let it Snow!

Olivia longed for snow. One morning when she woke up and looked out of her window, there it was – a **beautiful** blanket of snow covering her garden! She raced downstairs and ate her breakfast as quickly as possible. Olivia had plans that wouldn't wait. This year she was going to build the **best snowman ever!** Last year her neighbour, Jacob, had built a fantastic snowman. Everybody had admired it and the local newspaper had included a picture of it in a 'Winter Wonderland' snow feature. This year Olivia wanted *her* snowman to be the talk of the town.

Olivia set to work. She made a big snowball and rolled it through the snow watching it grow bigger and bigger, just as she had seen Jacob do the year before. Jacob was the best person she knew at **snowman** building, and she tried to remember exactly what he had done the year before. She was rolling another ball of snow for the head, when she realised something was missing. Where was Jacob? Surely he should be out by now, building his own snowman.

Olivia looked towards her neighbour's house and was surprised to see Jacob indoors and staring at her from behind the window.

She went over to his front door and instantly saw the problem – Jacob had a **broken arm!**

"I slipped on some ice last night," Jacob explained sadly. "The doctor said I need to rest my arm and keep it dry. Now I won't be able to build a snowman."

Olivia thought for a while and then smiled. "Wrap up warm and come outside," she told Jacob mysteriously.

Jacob sat grandly on the garden chair that Olivia had arranged for him, with his broken arm resting in a sling. Jacob gave Olivia instructions and she built the snowman just as he advised. The two friends made a great team, they just knew

they'd make this year's 'Winter Wonderland' snow feature.

The next morning, Olivia rushed downstairs to see the local newspaper. Sure enough, there was her and Jacob's fantastic snowman. As she rushed out to show Jacob, she realised that the snow was melting and their snowman was almost gone.

"Never mind," Jacob told her. "We can build another snowman together next time it snows."

"And we'll always have this fantastic newspaper picture to remind us of this one!" added Olivia.

The Wicked Queen

Once there lived a very wicked queen, whose husband the king was as **good** as she was wicked. But everyone said that the king was just a bit too good. In fact, he could only see good in people, and seemed blind to the evil deeds of his wicked wife.

One day, when the queen was in a **particularly** bad mood, she locked one of the servants in a cupboard. When the servant complained of this bad treatment to the king, he just said that it must have been a mistake.

"My lovely wife would never do such a dreadful thing," he told the servant.

The next day, a young maid was cleaning the queen's room. She was late finishing and knew she would be punished if the queen found her still there. So, when the poor young maid heard the queen approaching, she hid under the bed.

The maid peeped out and saw the queen enter the room. She was astonished to see the queen open up a golden box and take from it a **crystal** bottle. The queen opened the bottle and carefully poured three drops of liquid from it into a silver goblet.

"**Ha, ha!**" laughed the queen. "When the king drinks my magic potion, he sees only good things, and never sees the **misery** I create."

240

The maid could hardly believe her own eyes and knew that there was only one thing to do. She crept over to the golden box, opened the crystal bottle and tipped the contents of it into a plant pot. Then she quickly filled the bottle back up with water, and put it back in the golden box.

The next day, the queen put the usual three drops of potion into the king's silver goblet but, of course, it was just harmless water and her power over the good king was broken.

That day, the wicked queen had locked three children from the village in the castle dungeon for no good reason. When the children's parents came to complain to the king, he couldn't believe his ears.

"My wife would never do such a thing," he told them. But nevertheless, he went to check for himself and was shocked to find the children there.

When the brave little maid heard what had happened, she rushed off to see the king. She told him all about what she had seen in the wicked queen's room and about the magic potion. The king was furious to hear how the people of his kingdom had been treated. He discovered that the wicked queen was really a witch in disguise, and he banished her from his kingdom forever.

He, and his subjects, lived happily ever after.

A Magical Birthday!

Emily had been crossing off the days on her calendar for weeks, and now her special day was finally here – it was her birthday at long last!

"Wake up!" called Emily, rushing into her parents' room. But when she got there, a sorry sight met her eyes. Her mother was propped up in bed with a nose as red as a radish!

"A…a…atishoo! Happy birthday darling," sniffled her mum. "I've caught a bug. We'll have to cancel your party I'm afraid. You won't be able to get it ready all by yourself."

But Emily insisted that she wanted to at least try.

"OK," said her mum, doubtfully. "You can give it a go."

Emily put on her best party dress and set to work. She laid a pretty cloth on the table and emptied crisps, biscuits and sausage rolls onto plates.

Now for the cake! This was the trickiest part. Emily stirred together the ingredients and tipped the mixture into a cake tin.

Knowing that she was too young to use the oven, Emily skipped next door to fetch her neighbour, Mrs Kindly, to help her.

"Well I never, you have been busy!" gasped Mrs Kindly when she saw the state of the kitchen. There were splodges of cake batter all over the place and her lovely party dress

was covered in blobs of food.

"Oh, no!" sobbed Emily. "My birthday is ruined!" The sad birthday girl covered her face with her hands and began to cry. All of a sudden, there was a flash of light which made her look up. Emily could hardly believe her eyes but... yes, it was true! Her lovely old neighbour had sprouted wings and was holding a magic wand!

"I am your fairy godmother!" exclaimed the transformed Mrs Kindly. "Everybody has one, although they don't always know it. We're supposed to stay secret, but this is an emergency!"

With a few waves of her magic wand, Emily's fairy godmother put everything in order. A beautiful iced cake stood in the centre of a sparkling table of party food, and Emily's dress was as good as new!

The party was a huge success and, after the guests had left, Emily rushed into her mother's room to tell her all about it.

"Mrs Kindly is certainly a helpful woman," laughed Mum. "But fairy godmother might be stretching it a bit far!"

Whether her mother believed her or not, Emily knew that this had been her best birthday ever!

The Ugly Duckling

Mummy Duck was waiting for her new eggs to hatch. All of a sudden, one of the eggs made a tapping noise. Tap! Tap!

Mummy Duck called to the other ducks.

"My eggs are hatching. Come and see!"

One by one, out popped five chirpy little ducklings.

"What sweet little ducklings!" everyone sighed. Mummy Duck beamed with pride. Cheep! Cheep!

But the biggest egg of all still hadn't opened. And Mummy was sure she had only laid five eggs...

Craaaak! Just then the final egg burst open and out tumbled the last duckling. Everyone peered at it closely.

"Oh!" gasped Mummy Duck.

"Ooh!" spluttered the other ducks.

"What an ugly duckling!"quacked an old duck.

"He's not ugly!" said Mummy Duck. "He's special."

The ugly duckling hid his head under his wing.

The next day Mummy Duck took all her little ducks to the farmyard.

"Hello everyone,"

she called to the animals. "Meet my ducklings."

The five yellow ducklings proudly puffed out their pretty feathers.

"Ah," sighed the animals, "what lovely ducklings."

The ugly duckling waddled forward. "Hello," he said.

There was a moment's silence.

Then...

"He's so grey!" said all the animals who saw him.

"He's so clumsy!" mooed a cow.

"He's so big!" squawked a hen.

The ugly duckling sank to the ground as large teardrops rolled down his long beak and splashed on the ground.

The ugly duckling felt all alone. "Nobody wants me," he whispered. "I'd be better off running away." With a breaking heart, the poor little duckling waddled across the meadow, leaving the farm and his family far behind him.

Soon the ugly duckling arrived at a river. Two geese were dipping and diving for food.

"Excuse me," the ugly ducking began bravely, "have you seen any ducklings like me?" The geese shook their heads.

"You're the strangest looking duckling we've ever seen," they honked. The ugly duckling waddled away as fast as he could. He kept going until he came to a large lake.

"If nobody wants me, then I'll just hide here forever," sniffed the ugly duckling, making himself a little nest among the reeds.

All through the long winter, the ugly duckling hid in his lonely clump of reeds, ashamed to show his face. But spring soon arrived and he couldn't help but peer out of his hiding place to look at the pretty landscape.

A graceful swan paddled into view and the ugly duckling backed away, afraid he would be teased. Instead, the swan

swam up to him and nudged him gently with its beak.

"Why are you hiding here?" asked the swan, kindly. "Come and join the rest of us."

The ugly duckling was so shocked he almost fell into the water. Surely the swan must be talking to someone else. But just as the ugly duckling stood up, he caught sight of his reflection in the lake. He stopped, stared and gasped in amazement. His grey feathers were now snowy white!

Just then, a family of five young ducks waddled along the riverbank with their mother.

"Look at that beautiful swan!" they quacked, pointing at the ugly duckling.

Mummy Duck recognised her little ugly duckling at once. "I always knew he was special," she quacked.

The ugly duckling held his head high on his elegant neck, ruffled his beautiful white feathers and proudly paddled away after his new friends.

Snow White

One snowy day, a queen sat sewing by her window. She accidently pricked her finger with the needle, and three drops of blood fell on the snow. The queen looked at the bright red blood on the white snow, against the black wood of the window frame, and thought: "I wish I had a child with lips as **red** as blood, skin as **white** as snow and hair as **black** as ebony wood!"

Some time after that, the queen gave birth to a little girl with deep red lips, snowy-white skin and glossy hair as black as ebony. She called her Snow White.

Sadly, the queen died, and the king married again. His new wife was beautiful, but cruel and selfish. She had a magic mirror, and every day she looked into it and asked:

"Mirror, mirror, on the wall, who is the fairest one of all?" And every day the mirror replied, *"You, O Queen are the fairest of them all."*

But as Snow White grew up, she grew more beautiful. And so, one morning, the queen's mirror said to her: *"You, O Queen, are fair, it's true. But Snow White is much fairer than you."*

In a jealous rage, the queen called her huntsman. "Take Snow White into the forest and kill her," she told him.

The huntsman took Snow White to the edge of the forest, but he could not bear to hurt her. "Run away, child," he said.

Poor, frightened Snow White! She was all alone, lost in the forest, running for her life.

Towards nightfall, Snow White came to a little cottage deep in the woods. She knocked softly, but there was no answer, so she let herself in. Inside, Snow White found a table and seven tiny chairs. Upstairs there were seven little beds.

"I'm so tired," she yawned, and she lay down and fell asleep.

A while later, she woke with a start. Seven little men were standing round her bed.

"Who are you?" she asked them.

"We are the seven dwarfs who live here," said one of the little men. "We work in the mines all day. Who are you?"

"I am Snow White," she replied, and she told them her sad story. The dwarfs felt sorry for Snow White. "If you cook and clean for us," said the eldest dwarf, "you can stay here, and we will keep you safe."

Snow White gratefully agreed. When they left for work the next morning, the dwarfs made Snow White promise not to go out, or open the door, or speak to anyone.

Meanwhile, the queen was back at her magic mirror. But she was shocked by what it told her:

"You are the fairest here, it's true, but there is someone fairer than you. Deep in the forest, in a cosy den, Snow White lives with seven little men."

"What?" shrieked the queen. "Snow White is alive?" The queen, who was really a wicked witch, brewed a deadly potion and poisoned a rosy red apple. Then, disguising herself as an old woman, she set out for the seven dwarfs' cottage.

Snow White was busy in the kitchen when she saw an old woman at the window. "Try my lovely red apples!" the old woman croaked. And she handed the poisoned apple to Snow White.

She took a big bite... and fell down **dead.** The queen hurried home to her magic mirror. At last it gave her the answer she wanted: *"You, O Queen, are the fairest of them all!"*

The dwarfs wept bitterly when they found Snow White dead. They didn't want to bury her and so they put her in a glass coffin. They watched over her, day and night.

One day a prince came riding through the forest. When he saw Snow White, he instantly fell in love with her.

"Please let me take the coffin back to my castle," he begged the dwarfs, and they agreed.

As the prince's servants lifted the coffin, one of them stumbled, and the piece of apple that was stuck in Snow White's throat came loose. Snow White opened her eyes.

Snow White looked into the prince's kind, gentle eyes, and she knew she loved him, too.

And so they were married, with the dwarfs beside them. They all lived happily together in the prince's castle for the rest of their long lives.

Minnie and Winnie

Minnie and Winnie
Slept in a shell.
Sleep, little ladies!
And they slept well.

Pink was the shell within,
Silver without;
Sounds of the great sea
Wandered about.

Sleep, little ladies,
Wake not soon!
Echo on echo
Dies to the moon.

Two bright stars
Peeped into the shell.
"What are they dreaming of?
Who can tell?"

Started a green linnet
Out of the croft;
Wake, little ladies,
The sun is aloft!

Lady Moon

Lady Moon, Lady Moon,
Where are you roving?
Over the sea.
Lady Moon, Lady Moon,
Whom are you loving?
All that love me.
Are you not tired with
Rolling, and never
Resting to sleep?
Why look so pale,
And so sad, as for ever
Wishing to weep?

The Little Turtle Dove

High in the pine tree,
The little turtle dove
Made a little nursery
To please her little love.

"Coo," said the turtle dove,
"Coo," said she;
In the long, shady branches
Of the dark pine tree.

Hey, My Kitten

Hey, my kitten, my kitten,
And hey my kitten, my deary,
Such a sweet pet as this
There is not far nor neary.
Here we go up, up, up,
Here we go down, down, downy;
Here we go backwards and forwards,
And here we go round, round, roundy.

Dickery, Dickery, Dare

Dickery, dickery, dare,
The pig flew up in the air.
The man in brown
Soon brought him down!
Dickery, dickery, dare.

Clap Hands

Clap hands, Daddy's coming up the waggon way,
His pockets full of money, and his hands full of clay.

Pussycat Ate the Dumplings

Pussycat ate the dumplings,
Pussycat ate the dumplings,
Mamma stood by,
And cried, "Oh fie!
Why did you eat the dumplings?"

Mrs White

Mrs White had a fright
In the middle of the night.
She saw a ghost, eating toast,
Halfway up a lamp post.

The Case of the Crop Circles

Molly's dad was reading the newspaper. "Look at this!" he said, showing Molly a photo of some huge circles of flattened corn in Farmer Gilbert's cornfield.

"How did they get there?" asked Molly.

"No one knows, but some people say they were made by aliens," her dad replied, with a grin. "Perhaps a UFO landed on the cornfield one night!"

Molly couldn't stop thinking about the crop circles. She didn't believe they were made by aliens. It was a mystery, and she wanted to solve it.

By teatime, she had come up with a plan. "Carlos and I

have to do a bat watch project," she told her dad. "Would you come out with us one night to count bats? I thought we could go to Farmer Gilbert's cornfield."

Her dad smiled. "OK," he agreed. "As there's no school tomorrow, we'll go tonight."

They took a flask of hot cocoa with them up to the cornfield. The moon was shining brightly.

After a couple of hours of counting bats Molly began to feel tired. Her dad gave a loud snore beside her. Molly's own eyes began to close – and then she opened them wide again as she saw something move in the corn. She had almost missed it! Two teenage boys were creeping into the field.

Molly nudged her dad and Carlos. "Look!" she said. The boys started beating down the corn with their skateboards. They moved quickly to make a big circle.

Molly, Carlos and her dad walked over to them. "You can stop that right now!" her dad said.

The boys looked embarrassed. "We were only having a bit of fun," the boys replied. "We like reading about our crop circles in the newspaper."

"If you promise you won't do this again, we won't tell on you," Molly said.

"It's a deal," the boys said, looking relieved.

Next week, Molly ran to the local shop to buy the newspaper as soon as it came out.

"Look, Dad!" Molly showed him the latest photo of Farmer Gilbert's field. "No more crop circles. It says the aliens have left!"

Her dad smiled. "But we know better, don't we?" he said.

Egg Raiders

Zac and Lili lived in a nature reserve on Karlin Island. They loved living there. They had lots of fun and some brilliant adventures.

"Do you want to come with me to see the gannets?" Mum asked Zac and Lili one day.

"Yes, please!" they said together.

Gannets were rare sea birds that lived on Black Rock, a small craggy island nearby.

"I hope some of the eggs have hatched," said Lili, as they sailed over to Black Rock. "I can't wait to see the chicks!"

As soon as they had landed, Zac and Lili ran off to the other side of the island.

Suddenly, Zac grabbed Lili's arm. "Look at those men!" he said, pointing.

Lili looked. "Oh no! They're stealing the gannet eggs!" she gasped.

"We can't let them get away," said Zac. "We have to do something."

Zac started running towards the beach. "If we let their boat go they can't escape. Come on, Lili!" he called.

Lili followed him. They both ran as fast as they could.

They found the thieves' boat, moored on the beach.

It was difficult to untie the knot but at last they managed it. Lili and Zac watched the boat float away, and then went to tell Mum what was happening.

"Good work," she said, when she heard what they had done. Then she phoned the coastguard and told him about the thieves.

"I'll be right there," he said. "Leave those thieves to me."

The thieves were looking for their boat when the coastguard arrived.

"You two had better come with me," he said sternly, taking the eggs off them.

When the gannets saw the men being taken away, they started making loud calls.

"I think they're pleased the men are gone!" said Lili.

"Or maybe they're saying thank you – to you!" said Mum.

My Little Puppy

Everyone agreed that Isobel's little puppy, Patches, looked adorable. He had stumpy legs and a round, chubby tummy, silky-soft ears, lively brown eyes and a small patch just over his right eye.

Isobel loved Patches and Patches loved Isobel.

The only problem was that Patches was always getting himself – and Isobel – into trouble.

Lots of trouble!

On Monday, Patches chewed one of Dad's slippers… and the strap on Mum's new handbag.

"Can't that animal chew on his toy?" complained Dad.

"He doesn't like it," sighed Isobel, trying to give Patches the rubber bone she had bought for him. Patches put his paws on Isobel's hands and licked them.

"That tickles," giggled Isobel. It was impossible to be cross with Patches for long.

On Tuesday, Patches pulled the clothes off the washing line and dragged them through the soil. The clothes were all dirty.

"Oh, Patches, not again!" complained Dad.

"He was only trying to play," defended Isobel. "He's really sorry, aren't you, Patches?"

Patches barked and rolled over on his back, waving his legs in the air. Even Dad had to laugh.

On Wednesday, Patches knocked over a vase.

"He was only trying to smell the flowers," said Isobel.

Patches put his head on one side and barked softly.

"See," said Isobel. "He's saying 'sorry,' aren't you, Patches?"

Mum grinned. "All right, but be more careful!"

Later that day Mrs May, who lived next door, was in her garden. Her white cat, Snowy, jumped on top of the fence and hissed at Patches.

Patches barked back.

"Please don't let that naughty puppy frighten poor Snowy," called Mrs May.

"We'll make sure Patches stays out of Snowy's way," said Mum.

"Yes, please do," sniffed Mrs May. "Poor Snowy!"

"Poor Snowy, indeed," muttered Isobel. "That cat is always teasing Patches."

"Now, now, Isobel," soothed Mum. "Mrs May was telling me earlier that she's lost her gold ring. I think her husband gave it to her a long time ago. She's very upset about it, and that probably makes her seem more cross than she really is. And you know she loves Snowy as much as you love Patches."

Mum was right. Mrs May and Snowy were best friends.

The next day Isobel and Patches were in the garden with Mum and Dad when Mrs May came out of her house.

"Any sign of your ring?" called Mum. Mrs May shook her head sadly. "I think I've lost it for good," she said.

Just then, Snowy jumped down from the fence, scratched Patches across his nose with her paw, then ran off.

"Snowykins!" cried Mrs May. "Naughty puss!"

Patches squeezed through a hole in the fence and began to chase Snowy round and round Mrs May's garden. Isobel and her parents followed. Round and round they went – till Dad caught Patches.

"Oh, no! Look at my vegetables!" cried Mrs May. "And my poor flowers!"

"We're so sorry," said Isobel's mum. "We'll help you replant them."

"That would be very kind," said Mrs May.

Mum and Mrs May picked up the plant pots and the gardening tools. Dad tied together the runner-bean canes that had been knocked over. And Isobel and Patches dug holes to put back some of the flowers that had been disturbed.

"What's that, Patches?" asked Isobel, as Patches pushed a lump of soil towards her with his nose. Isobel scraped away the soil, then leaped to her feet.

"Mrs May! Mrs May! Patches has found your ring!"

Mrs May was delighted. "Oh, you clever puppy!" she said, patting Patches' head. "How can I ever thank you?"

And after that, Isobel, Patches and Mrs May were the best of friends.

Even though Patches still sometimes chased naughty Snowy round and round the garden!

Dolphin Finds a Star

One night in the moonlight, a baby dolphin called Splash looked up and saw a shooting star. It zoomed across the sky and disappeared.

"That star has fallen into the water!" Splash cried. "I'm going to find it and give it to my mummy as a present. She loves shiny things."

In the distance Splash saw something sparkling. He swam towards the sparkles, thinking it was the star.

But when he got closer, he saw that it was a shoal of flashing fish, wiggling and weaving through the water.

Then Splash saw something glowing above his head. "There's the star! My mummy will be so pleased," he thought happily, and he swam towards the shining light.

But when he got closer, Splash found that the light was a lamp shining on the very top of a sailing boat.

The more the baby dolphin swam around, the more shiny creatures he saw. There were flashing fish, jiggly jellyfish and even sparkly seahorses, but the fallen star was nowhere to be found.

At last, Splash saw a light that was much brighter than all the rest. He swam towards it, hoping it would be the star. He swam through an underwater garden of swirling seaweed and shimmering shells. And then, at last, he found the star. It was in the hair of a beautiful mermaid queen sitting on her throne.

"Hello, baby dolphin. What brings you here?" she asked, but Splash felt very shy. He didn't know what to say.

So the flashing fish, the jiggly jellyfish and the sparkly seahorses all told the mermaid queen:

"He was looking for the star that's in your hair. He wanted to give it to his mummy."

"In that case, you shall have it," said the mermaid, and she handed the shining star to Splash.

Splash gave his mummy the star and she was very pleased.

Together they played with it all day long.

Then, when night came, they jumped up as high as they could and pushed the star back up into the sky, where it could shine down on everyone – on the flashing fish and the jiggly jellyfish, on the sparkly seahorses and on you, too.

Cats and Dogs

Hoddley, poddley, puddle and fogs,
Cats are to marry the poodle dogs;
Cats in blue jackets and dogs in red hats,
What will become of the mice and the rats?

I Bought an Old Man

Hey diddle diddle,
And hey diddle dan!
And with a little money,
I bought an old man.
His legs were all crooked
And wrong ways set on,
So what do you think
Of my little old man?

Hearts

Hearts, like doors, will open with ease
To very, very, little keys,
And don't forget that two of these
Are "I thank you" and "If you please".

New Hay

Willy boy, Willy boy,
Where are you going?
I will go with you,
If that I may.
I'm going to the meadow
To see them a-mowing,
I am going to help them
Turn the new hay.

Two Little Dogs

Two little dogs
Sat by the fire
Over a fender of coal-dust;
Said one little dog
To the other little dog,
If you don't talk, why, I must.

Mother Shuttle

Old Mother Shuttle
Lived in a coal-scuttle
Along with her dog and her cat;
What they ate I can't tell,
But 'tis known very well
That not one of the party was fat.

Little Husband

I had a little husband,
No bigger than my thumb;
I put him in a pint pot
And there I bade him drum.
I gave him some garters
To garter up his hose,
And a little silk handkerchief
To wipe his pretty nose.

The Robins

A robin and a robin's son
Once went to town to buy a bun.
They couldn't decide on a plum or plain,
And so they went back home again.

The Merchants of London

Hey diddle dinkety, poppety, pet,
The merchants of London they wear scarlet;
Silk in the collar and gold in the hem,
So merrily march the merchant men.

The Dame of Dundee

There was an old woman,
Who lived in Dundee,
And in her back garden
There was a plum tree;
The plums they grew rotten
Before they grew ripe,
And she sold them
Three farthings a pint.

Christmas Eve

On Christmas Eve I turned the spit,
I burnt my fingers, I feel it yet;
The little cock sparrow flew over the table,
The pot began to play with the ladle.

Gingerbread Men

Smiling girls, rosy boys,
Come and buy my little toys:
Monkeys made of gingerbread,
And sugar horses painted red.

Fairy Daisy

Daisy was the most playful little fairy in Fairyland. She was as fresh as a spring morning and always **giggling**.

The smaller fairies all loved playing with Daisy. She always thought of games that were such fun!

"Come and play with us," called three little fairies to Daisy one day. Daisy had just been given her first **magic** wand and was busy practising how to use it.

"Look at me," giggled Daisy. "I'm making magic flowers grow." The three little fairies ran up to their favourite fairy to take a closer look. "Can we have a go?" they asked.

"You're too little to use a magic wand," Daisy told them. "But I can think of a game that will be great fun!"

Daisy waved her new wand over one of the little fairies and there was a **magical** puff of green mist. When the mist cleared, the other two fairies both laughed to see that Daisy had turned their friend a lovely shade of **pea green!**

"Me next! Me next!" the other two fairies called. Daisy used her new magic wand to turn the little fairies into all the colours of the **rainbow.** It was terrific fun and they all laughed until they were out of breath.

They had all been so busy playing, that nobody had noticed how late it had got. The little fairies had to go home for their lunch. "You can change us back now," they said.

But when Daisy tried to change them back to their usual colour, she couldn't make her spell work. First she made them **spotty** and, when she tried again, she made them **stripy!**

"Oh no!" cried the playful fairy. "Whatever will your mothers say?"

Daisy took her little friends home and explained what had happened. Luckily their mothers were better at using magic wands than Daisy was, and turned them all back to normal. Daisy didn't get into too much **trouble,** but from then on she was known as Whoops-a-Daisy!

Princess in Peril

There was once a happy-go-lucky princess whose name was Wanda.

One hot summer's day, Princess Wanda went for a ride on Snowy, her favourite horse. The sun shone brightly and, as she rode along, Princess Wanda sang happily to the rhythm of Snowy's hooves as they clip-clopped along the path. Soon, the palace where she lived was just a speck in the distance and the sun was going down, but still the carefree princess rode on.

Feeling adventurous, she and Snowy rode into some woods. The air was cooler under the tree tops, and Princess Wanda climbed down off her horse and sat beneath the shady branches while Snowy grazed lazily on some grass.

Suddenly there was a loud cackle and a witch jumped out from behind a nearby tree, as if from nowhere. Snowy was so frightened that she bolted away, back down the path and towards her home at the palace.

"Ha, ha!" cackled the wicked witch as she pointed her magic wand at the frightened princess. "You are my prisoner now!" And as the wand cast its magical light over Princess Wanda, she found that she was unable to resist as the wicked witch led her to a castle and locked her in a room, high up in a tower.

Then, the wicked witch took the golden locket from around Princess Wanda's neck. "This will do very nicely," she cackled. "I will send it to your father as proof that you are my prisoner. He will have to give me lots of gold if he wants his precious daughter back!"

Back at Princess Wanda's palace, Snowy had returned without her and everyone was very worried.

"Where can my little princess be?" sobbed her poor mother.

When the king and queen received Princess Wanda's golden necklace with a message from the wicked witch, the king wanted to send his army out to fetch her. But the royal wizard, Enigmo, warned the king that the witch's magic was very powerful, and told him that even an entire army would be no good against her powerful magic.

"Don't worry, I'll find Princess Wanda and bring her back home," promised Enigmo.

He set off right away, flying on the back of his enchanted dragon. Enigmo and the dragon flew away from the royal palace and over the shady woods, determined to find the lost princess and defeat the witch. They flew for many hours, scanning the wooded ground beneath them, but they could not see any trace of the princess or the witch.

"I felt sure that the witch's castle was in these woods," sighed Enigmo. Just as the young wizard and his dragon were about to fly away, the wizard heard a beautiful sound. An enchanting melody floated up into the air, and Enigmo recognised it at once.

"It's Princess Wanda!" Enigmo explained to his dragon. "The witch must have put an invisibility spell on the castle to stop us finding her, but her magic wasn't enough to stop

Princess Wanda's beautiful voice from escaping."

Following the lovely sound, Enigmo and his dragon swooped down through the invisibility barrier until they could see the castle, with Princess Wanda waving to them from the tower.

"I'll be back for you very soon," called Enigmo to Princess Wanda, as she greeted him from the window. "But first I must defeat the wicked witch so that she can never work her evil magic again!"

The dragon glided gently to the ground. Enigmo climbed down from his scaly back and set off to find the witch.

Enigmo crept into the castle, searching for the witch. He peeped around a door and saw the witch cackling to herself and dancing about.

"When the king brings me his gold, I will be **rich.** I will make that foolish king my prisoner, too, and then I will be in charge of everything," she said.

Enigmo mumbled a spell and, before the witch had time to notice him, she was transformed into a **frog,** and her magic wand clattered to the ground.

"That wicked witch can do no more harm now," Enigmo told the princess, as he helped her up onto the dragon's back.

When Princess Wanda arrived home, the king and queen were delighted. They threw a fantastic **party** to celebrate, and Enigmo and his dragon were the guests of honour.

The Magic Pie

Once upon a time, a kind woman baked a pie and shared it with her friends. But when she went to wash the empty dish – she couldn't **believe** her eyes! The pie was still there as if it had just come out of the oven. The next day she shared the pie with some hungry travellers and, when she went to wash the dish, she saw once again that the pie was still there.

News of the magic pie spread, and many hungry people came to be fed by the kind woman's **magic** pie.

A **greedy** king heard about the magic pie and wanted it for himself. He sent his soldiers to fetch the pie, and they took it to the royal kitchen. A butler placed the pie beneath a silver dome and went straight to the king to present it to him. The king licked his lips and lifted the dome... but the pie was **gone!** All that remained of it was a pile of mouldy dust.

The king vowed never to eat pie again and, as for the kind woman? Well, she just baked another pie!

The Singing Princess

There was once a princess called Melody who would not stop singing. She sang all day and half of the night. Although she had a pretty voice, the whole palace was fed up with it and begged her to stop. But the princess just went on singing.

The king decided to build Princess Melody a little house in the palace grounds where she could sing to her heart's content without disturbing anyone.

One day, the princess was singing her heart out and her song went soaring into the sky. A travelling knight heard the tune and began to sing along.

"What beautiful music!" thought the knight.

He rode on and the song became louder as he got nearer to the princess.

As the princess sang she became aware of another voice joining in. Together the two voices merged as one and sounded beautiful. Before long, the two singers found themselves face to face.

"I'm Princess Melody," sang the princess.

"I'm Sir Harmony," replied the knight.

The two singers fell in love and were married. They made beautiful music together and lived happily ever after.

The Musicians of Bremen

Once upon a time, a farmer had a donkey which was old and unfit and he wanted to get rid of it. The donkey, who was a clever beast, decided to run away and become a musician. So he set off for the town of Bremen.

The donkey hadn't walked far, when he found a dog lying on the road, **panting and gasping** to get his breath.

"Why are you panting so hard?" asked the donkey.

"Ah," puffed the hound. "As I'm so old, my master wanted to get rid of me, so I ran away."

"Hey, why don't you join me?" said the donkey. "I'm going to Bremen to become a musician."

The old dog quickly agreed, and they went on together.

After they had walked a short distance, they heard a cat **meowing** sorrowfully.

"Oh dear," said the donkey. "What's wrong with you?"

"As I'm too old to catch mice, my mistress wanted to get rid of me, so I ran away. " he said.

"Come with us to Bremen. You sing beautifully and will make a fine musician." said the donkey. The cat thought this sounded like a splendid idea and decided to join them.

They set off again and soon met a cockerel. "Cock-a-doodle-doo!" he crowed. "My mistress wants to feed me to her guests," he continued, sadly.

"We can't let that happen," said the donkey. "You'd better come with us. We're off to town to become musicians. You could sing with us." The cockerel quickly agreed, and all four carried on down the road.

That evening, the donkey and dog settled down beneath a tree. The cat settled on a low branch. And the cockerel flew to the top of the tree, where it was safest. Before settling down, the cockerel looked around and saw a light in the distance.

"There's a house not far from here," he called to his new friends. "I can see lights."

So, instead of sleeping beneath the tree, they made their way to the house, which was glowing with lights.

The donkey, being the biggest, peered through the window.

"What do you see?" asked the cockerel.

"A table covered with good things to eat and drink, and thieves sitting around enjoying themselves."

"This would be a perfect place for us to live," said the cat. And they all came up with a plan to get rid of the robbers.

The animals climbed on top of each other and began to perform their music:

"Eeee-ooar!" the donkey brayed.
"Woof! Woof!" the dog barked.
"Meow! Meow!" the cat mewed.
"Cock-a-doodle-doo!" the cockerel crowed.

Then they all burst in through the window, scattering the robbers in all directions. The thieves, who thought that some horrible monster had come for them, scampered away as fast as they could.

The four animals sat down at the thieves' table and ate, and ate.

Then they turned out the lights and searched for a bed. The donkey lay down on some straw in the yard. The dog lay on the mat beside the door. The cat curled up in front of the fire. And the cockerel perched on top of the chimney. They all fell swiftly to sleep.

But the thieves hadn't run far and, when they saw that the house was dark, one of them went back to investigate.

The thief found the house still and quiet, so he went into the kitchen to light a candle. When he saw the **fiery** eyes of the cat glittering in the fireplace, he thought they were hot coals and held some paper to them to get a light. The cat was **furious** and flew at his face. The thief ran for the door, but the dog, who lay there, sprang up and bit his leg. The injured thief raced across the yard, where

the donkey kicked him smartly on his backside. Then the cockerel, who had been awakened by the noise, crowed with all his might. The terrified thief ran back to the other thieves.

"There's a **terrible** witch in the house," he told his friends. "She spat at me and scratched my face with her long claws. Then there was a man by the door who stabbed me in the leg with a knife. And a monster in the yard who beat me with a wooden club. And on the roof there's a demon judge, who called out, 'COOK THE CROOK DO.' So I ran away while I still could."

After that night, the robbers never again dared to return to the house. And it suited the four musicians so well that they decided to stay. I expect that they are still there now.

Fairy Seasons

Spring fairies laugh and play,
Hopping and skipping
With bunnies all day.
Hop, skip, hop, skip,
To make the garden happy.
Summer fairies flutter around,
Cleaning and shining
The flowers on the ground.
Softly, softly, clean and shine,
To make the garden pretty.
Autumn fairies dance round the trees,
Catching and chasing

The leaves in the breeze.
Hurry, scurry, catch the leaves,
To make the garden tidy.
Winter fairies float through the air,
Sprinkling and shaking
Snow here and there.
Gently, gently, spread the snow,
To make the garden sparkle.
Then, once a year, as a special treat,
The fairy queen and the fairies meet.
They sing and dance to celebrate
The magic in the garden.

In the Tree-top

Rock-a-bye, baby, up in the tree-top!
Mother his blanket is spinning;
And a light little rustle that never will stop,
Breezes and boughs are beginning.
Rock-a-bye, baby, swinging so high!
Rock-a-bye!

When the wind blows, then the cradle will rock.
Hush! now it stirs in the bushes;
Now with a whisper, a flutter of talk,
Baby and hammock it pushes.
Rock-a-bye, baby! Shut, pretty eye!
Rock-a-bye!

Mother Hubbard

Old Mother Hubbard went to the cupboard
To get her poor doggy a bone;
But when she came there the cupboard was bare,
And so the poor doggy had none.

She went to the tailor's
To buy him a coat
But when she came back
He was riding a goat.

She went to the cobbler's
To buy him some shoes,
But when she came back
He was reading the news.

She went to the hosier's
To buy him some hose
When she came back
He was dressed in his clothes.

The dame made a curtsey,
The dog made a bow,
The dame said, "Your servant,"
The dog said, "Bow wow."

The Enchanted Princess

There was once a king and queen who had such a beautiful baby daughter that the Fairy Queen came to hear of it.

"This must be a very special child indeed to be so utterly beautiful," the Fairy Queen thought to herself. And she sent three of her best fairies to give her three magical gifts. The first fairy gave her the gift of wisdom, the second gave the gift of honesty and the third gift was charity.

The king and queen had no idea how special their baby was.

By the time the princess had grown into a young lady, news of her beauty had spread far and wide. Every prince in the world wanted to marry her and, although those that came to meet her were either rich or handsome, the princess did not fall in love with any of them. The king and queen were worried.

"You have the pick of every prince in the world, surely one of them will do," sighed the perplexed queen.

"But mother," replied the princess, "I must be honest with myself. I must marry a worthy man."

Being a wise young woman, the princess realised that these princes only wanted her for her beautiful face so, when the princes came to visit her again, she made herself look ugly by placing a large **wart** from the skin of a pig on the end of her nose.

One by one the princes came to see her, but this time none proposed marriage because they were put off by the enormous wart. It was not until the last prince of all came to visit the princess that she finally met a man **worthy** of her love. This prince was from a far-off land and it had taken him many weeks to reach the princess's palace. As soon as she met him, the princess knew that he was the one, for he did not even glance at her face, but seemed to **gaze** straight into her heart.

"This is the prince I shall marry," declared the princess.

"But my dear child," replied the queen. "You cannot marry this prince, for he is **blind.**"

But because the princess had the gifts of wisdom, honesty and charity, she followed her heart and married the blind prince. She realised that true beauty comes from within and that real vision doesn't always come from the eyes. So she and her prince lived happily ever after.

Sweet Dreams

Princess Isabella could not sleep. Every time she rested her head on her pillow and began to doze off, she had a bad dream that **woke** her up. The little princess hadn't slept well for weeks, nor had her parents who always went to comfort her when she woke up.

"**Mummy!**" called Isabella. "I had another bad dream. It was about a monster that was coming to eat me up and I couldn't run away from it!"

And so the broken nights continued until everyone had dark circles around their eyes from lack of sleep.

"If only we could stop these bad dreams our little girl keeps having," sighed the queen one evening, as she stood by an open window. Little did she know that the Night Fairies were out and about spreading spells of kindness and happiness. There was one young fairy just outside the queen's window, who overheard what the queen had said.

The little Night Fairy knew that this was a bigger task than she could manage all by herself and so she flew off to fetch her fairy friends.

Unseen, the fairies flew into the palace and waved their **magic wands** over **everyone.** Soon there was not a sound to be heard throughout the whole palace as everyone was **sleeping peacefully,** including little Princess Isabella.

"What wonderful dreams I had last night," yawned the little princess when she woke up. "I dreamed that I was at a wonderful party in Fairyland, and that I could fly."

That night, the princess went to bed quite happily, in the hope that she would dream more **sweet** dreams, and she was not disappointed!

That very night she dreamed that she slid down a rainbow and landed in a **mermaid lagoon.** The night after that she dreamed about a wonderful orchard where the fruit was all made of chocolate.

The Night Fairies had worked their magic and Princess Isabella never had another bad dream again.

She, her parents and indeed the whole palace always slept very well!

The Spooky Shipwreck

There was great excitement under the sea. There had been a storm in the night with very big waves and, when the sea had become calm again, Zippy the dolphin had found a shipwreck.

"Let's explore it!" suggested Zippy to his friends, and they all swam in through a porthole.

"It must have sunk years ago," said Zippy. "I expect the storm swept it in."

Suddenly there was a shriek of excitement.

"Come and see what I've found!" called Delores the jellyfish. Everyone swam over to take a look.

"Treasure!" gasped Zippy. "Perhaps this was a pirate ship."

"I hope there are no ghosts," said Delores, wobbling at the thought. "It's spooky here, I'm not sure that I like it."

"There are no such things as ghosts," said Zippy, doing his best to reassure her. But just then, Zippy and Delores heard a strange clicking sound. Click! Click! The sound was coming closer and closer towards them.

"W-w-what could it be?" stammered Delores. "It sounds like a peg-legged pirate coming this way!"

Zippy and Delores hid behind the treasure chest, shivering with fear. Click! Click! Click! Whatever was making the spooky sound was almost there. Bravely, Zippy peeped out from behind the treasure.

"Ha! It's only our friend Wanda the lobster, coming to see the treasure!" laughed Zippy.

Wanda admired the treasure as it glinted through the water. "It's so pretty! I wonder what we should do with it."

The sea creatures decided to ask King Neptune what they should do, and swam off to his palace.

"Treasure, eh?" boomed Neptune. "I've got too much treasure already, I don't need any more. You have my permission to do what you like with it!"

At first the sea creatures couldn't think of anything to do with their exciting find, and then Wanda had a fantastic idea. "We all had such fun playing in the shipwreck this morning, so let's open a Spooky Pirate theme park and then everyone can join in the fun!" said the little lobster, who was pink with excitement.

So the friends dressed up as pirates and invited all the creatures of the sea to come along and see the sunken ship and its treasure. And the most popular attraction at the theme park was The Clicking Peg-legged Ghost. Wanda had to click her claws so often that they got rather sore!

Rapunzel

Once, a man and his wife were expecting a baby. A witch lived next door and had a garden which was full of rapunzel plants. The woman had such a longing to eat the tasty leaves.

"I just must eat rapunzel leaves," said the wife.

So the man went into the witch's garden and picked the leaves to satisfy his wife's craving.

The man picked the leaves every day, but one day the witch caught him. "Why are you stealing my leaves?" she said.

"My wife is expecting a baby and she has such a craving for rapunzel leaves," replied the man.

"You can have my leaves," said the witch, "but you must give me your baby."

When the baby was born, the man gave the baby to the witch, who called her Rapunzel.

Rapunzel grew into a beautiful woman with long hair. The witch took Rapunzel to a tower that had one window, but no door.

The witch would come to the tower and call, *"Rapunzel, Rapunzel, let down your hair."*

Rapunzel would let down her long

hair, and the witch would climb up it.

One day, a prince came by and heard Rapunzel singing. He wanted to get into the tower, but when he saw there was no door he hid, waited and watched.

After a while, the prince saw the witch and heard her call to Rapunzel. He watched as the witch climbed up and, when the witch had gone, he called, *"Rapunzel, Rapunzel, let down your hair."*

The prince climbed up and, when he saw Rapunzel, he fell in love. The prince visited her every day.

But the witch soon found out and was very angry.

She cut off Rapunzel's hair and sent her far away.

When the prince next came to visit, the witch let down Rapunzel's cut-off hair and the prince climbed up. When he saw the witch, he let go and fell down into a thorny bush. Sharp thorns went into his eyes, and he could no longer see.

The blind prince walked and walked until one day, he heard Rapunzel singing, and the two were reunited.

When Rapunzel heard what had happened to the prince, she cried, and her tears fell into the prince's eyes, washing away the thorns. The prince could see again! The prince and Rapunzel were married, and they lived happily ever after.

The Wedding

Pussycat, wussicat, with a white foot,
When is your wedding and I'll come to it.
The beer's to brew, and the bread's to bake,
Pussycat, wussicat, don't be too late.

First

First in a carriage,
Second in a gig,
Third on a donkey,
And fourth on a pig.

Gee Up, Neddy

Gee up, Neddy,
Don't you stop,
Just let your feet go
Clippety clop.
Clippety clopping,
Round and round.
Giddy up,
We're homeward bound.

Slowly, Slowly

Slowly, slowly, very slowly
Creeps the garden snail.
Slowly, slowly, very slowly
Up the garden rail.

Quickly, quickly, very quickly
Runs the little mouse.
Quickly, quickly, very quickly
Round about the house.

Hark! Hark!

Hark, hark,
The dogs do bark,
Beggars are coming to town:
Some in rags,
Some in tags,
And some in velvet gowns.

The Little Bird

This little bird flaps its wings,
Flaps its wings, flaps its wings,
This little bird flaps its wings,
And flies away in the morning!

What Do You Think?

There was an old woman, and what do you think?
She lived upon nothing but victuals and drink:
Victuals and drink were the chief of her diet;
This tiresome old woman could never be quiet.

The Baby in the Cradle

The baby in the cradle
Goes rock-a-rock-a-rock.
The clock on the dresser
Goes tick-a-tick-a-tock.

The rain on the window
Goes tap-a-tap-a-tap,
But here comes the sun,
So we clap-a-clap-a-clap!

A Cat Came Fiddling

A cat came fiddling out of a barn,
With a pair of bagpipes under her arm;
She could sing nothing but, "Fiddle cum fee,
The mouse has married the bumble-bee."
Pipe, cat – dance, mouse,
We'll have a wedding at our good house.

Bobby Shaftoe

Bobby Shaftoe's gone to sea,
Silver buckles at his knee;
When he comes back
He'll marry me,
Bonny Bobby Shaftoe!

Dance to Your Daddy

Dance to your daddy,
My little babby;
Dance to your daddy,
My little lamb.

You shall have a fishy,
In a little dishy;
You shall have a fishy
When the boat comes in.

Teeth

Thirty white horses upon a red hill,
Now they tramp, now they champ,
Now they stand still.

Neptune's Surprise!

It was King Neptune's birthday and the seabed was buzzing with excitement. The merfolk had decided to throw a surprise party for their king, and everyone was busy wrapping presents and thinking of **surprises** for him.

Mimi the oyster had made Neptune a lovely shiny pearl, and some of the mermaids had baked a cake. But there was one little mermaid who was feeling sad. Mya wanted to find a very **special** present, but she couldn't think of anything to give her king. She was sitting all by herself still wondering what to do, when Snapper the crab sidled up to her to see why she wasn't busy getting ready for the party.

"Oh dear," sighed poor Mya. "I can't think of anything to give King Neptune. All the best ideas have gone."

"Don't worry," said Snapper. "There must be something special that you can give him." The friendly crab clicked his claws while he tried to think – Clickety, click! But neither of them could come up with a new idea.

"What are you giving Neptune?" Mya asked Snapper.

"I'm playing him a tune on my keyboard," he replied. "Basher Octopus, Jazzy Blowfish and Rocker Seahorse are playing too."

"Oh, how wonderful," gasped Mya. "Neptune will love that!"

"The only problem is that none of us can sing," sighed Snapper, "and we really wanted to sing 'Happy Birthday!' to him."

Mya perked up when she heard this, and Snapper couldn't understand why.

"You'll just have to wait and see!" Mya told him mysteriously, when he asked.

The party started and Neptune sat happily on his throne enjoying the wonderful surprise. Snapper and his band played some great tunes and everybody danced merrily. After a while, Mya made her way towards the stage and climbed up to join the band. She whispered something in Snapper's ear and then walked to the front.

Mya's voice rang out as she sang 'Happy Birthday!' to Neptune. She had a beautiful voice and everyone clapped and cheered. Nobody cheered louder than Neptune, who declared Mya's song the best present of all!

The Boy Next Door

Abigail had known the boy next door for as long as she could remember. His name was Andrew and they had played together when they were little. But now they liked different things from each other. Andrew often teased Abigail when she played with her dolls or had her friends round for a sleepover.

One day, Abigail was walking home from school when she heard Andrew riding up behind her on his bike.

"Hey, carrot-top!" he called to her. "Are you entering the poetry competition tomorrow?"

Abigail hated to be teased about her auburn hair, and **blushed** scarlet. She turned into her garden gate and hurried up the path to her door without replying.

Abigail was going to enter the poetry competition. She had written a **wonderful** poem about her pet cat to read out.

That night, Abigail's mother gave her a long, yellow dress to wear for the competition.

"I wore this dress when I was your age," explained Abigail's mother. "It brought me luck when I entered a competition and I thought it might do the same for you."

Abigail sighed. It was a lovely

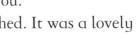

dress, but she was worried that
Andrew would **tease** her about it.

The next day, Abigail was
nervous about the competition
all day. When the time came for
the competition to begin, Abigail
changed into her yellow dress and
went backstage to wait for her
turn.

Then Abigail spotted Andrew.
She tried to **hide** behind a
curtain but Andrew spotted her and came over.

This time he was the one to blush. "H-h-hello, Abigail," he
stammered. "G-gosh! You look lovely in your dress." Andrew
realised that Abigail was turning into a pretty young lady and
that he didn't want to tease her at all.

The two neighbours shook hands, wished each other luck
and waited **nervously** for their turns. When the time came,
each of them read their poems well and received loud applause.
When the winners were to be announced, Abigail and Andrew
stood next to each other waiting for the result.

"We have joint winners for this competition," announced
the head teacher. "Abigail and Andrew share first place. They
were both so good that the judges couldn't choose between
them!" Andrew and Abigail were so pleased, not just about
winning – they had discovered that they still had something in
common. Now they could be friends again!

The Best of Friends

Cleo the horse and Daphne Duck were the best of friends. They never ever argued... well, **hardly** ever!

One rainy day when the friends were stuck indoors, Daphne and Cleo were feeling bored.

"I've got a good idea, let's play with building blocks," quacked Daphne.

"Neigh! I've got a better idea – why don't we put on a show?" whinnied Cleo. "I could do my special tap-dance and you could tell some of your funny jokes!"

"That's a good idea, but I'd really prefer to play with the building blocks right now," replied Daphne.

"**Show!**" shouted Cleo.

"**Blocks!**" shouted back Daphne.

The two best friends just couldn't agree what to do.

"Well, I'm playing with the building blocks," snapped Daphne. "I can quite easily play by myself!" And she set to work building a lovely tower from the blocks.

"Neigh! Suit yourself," said Cleo, and she started galloping around the room practising her tap-dancing. "I'll put on my own show, so there!"

Daphne was just finishing her beautiful tower made from the blocks when, all of a sudden, Cleo came tippety-tapping across the room – **crash!**

Cleo fell right on top of Daphne's tower and landed in a heap of blocks. Daphne was furious.

"I'm sorry," said Cleo rubbing her nose where a block had landed on it. "I'll help you to re-build it." Daphne was still feeling rather cross, but agreed to let Cleo help. The two friends set to work.

"Why don't we build something different this time?" suggested Daphne.

"What would you like to build?" asked Cleo.

"Well... er... how about a lovely stage?" said Daphne. "Then we could put on that show you were talking about."

The two friends set to work. Soon they had built a lovely stage. It didn't really matter that there was no audience. Cleo and Daphne put on a wonderful show. Cleo's tap-dance was followed by Daphne's comedy act.

"What time does a duck wake up?" joked Daphne. "At the quack of dawn!"

Cleo laughed so much that she made the stage **fall** down. But it didn't matter, they'd soon think of another game to play together!

Jingle's Bell!

Jingle was Lottie's best toy of all. He wasn't exactly a bear and he wasn't quite a bunny. He had a **bell** in one ear, which was how he'd got his name.

One day, Lottie woke up to find it had snowed overnight. She was very excited and grabbed Jingle by the paw to take him with her for a closer look.

All Lottie's friends were out, and ready for some fun. The games went on all morning, until Lottie was called in for lunch by her mother.

"See you later," she called. And she looked around for Jingle. Soft white mounds of snow had covered everything and, although she looked everywhere, she couldn't find him.

"Don't worry," said Lottie's mum. "We know he's out there somewhere, we're sure to find him later." But although everyone searched through the afternoon, there was simply too much snow and Jingle remained lost.

It was nearly **bedtime** and Lottie was getting really worried.

"How will I be able to sleep without Jingle?" she sighed, staring out of the window still hoping to spot her soft friend. As she sat there she noticed a little bird pecking at the snow.

"Poor little thing," said Lottie's mum. "I expect he's

looking for something to eat."

As the bird continued to peck the ground, Lottie heard a strange sound. It was a kind of **muffled** tinkle. Had she imagined it? No, there it it was again!

"Can you hear that sound?" Lottie asked, but her mum couldn't hear anything.

Suddenly, Lottie **jumped** up off her chair. She had just realised what the sound could be. She rushed out into her garden, not even stopping to put on her coat and wellies.

"Hey! Where are you rushing off to?" called Lottie's mum.

Lottie ran over to where the little bird had been pecking and dug with her bare hands, hoping her hunch was right.

Yes, there he was! She could see his little ear **poking** up through the snow, and she kept on digging until she could pull out her cold, soggy friend.

Lottie had got nearly as cold and wet as Jingle, and they both sat by the fire to warm up. Lottie sipped at her hot chocolate drink.

"I told you he'd show up," smiled Lottie's mum.

"He was **saved** by his bell!" laughed Lottie.

And that night, she gave her friend such a big hug that it nearly squeezed his stuffing out!

Pussycat, Pussycat

Pussycat, pussycat, where have you been?
I've been up to London to visit the Queen.
Pussycat, pussycat, what did you there?
I frightened a little mouse under her chair.

Silly Sally

Silly Sally swiftly shooed seven silly sheep.
The seven silly sheep Silly Sally shooed shilly-shallied south.
These sheep shouldn't sleep in a shack;
Sheep should sleep in a shed.

Rock-a-Bye, Baby

Rock-a-bye, baby, thy cradle is green;
Father's a nobleman, Mother's a queen,
And Betty's a lady and wears a gold ring,
And Johnny's a drummer and drums for the King.

There Was an Old Woman

There was an old woman lived under a hill,
And if she's not gone she lives there still.

Frisky Lamb

A frisky lamb
And a frisky child
Playing their pranks
In a cowslip meadow:
The sky all blue
And the air all mild
And the fields all sun
And the lanes half-shadow.

Frog Went a-Courtin'

Mr Froggie went a-courtin' an' he did ride;
Sword and pistol by his side.
He went to Missus Mousie's hall,
Gave a loud knock and gave a loud call.

"Pray, Missus Mousie, air you within?"
"Yes, kind sir, I set an' spin."
He tuk Miss Mousie on his knee,
An' sez, "Miss Mousie, will ya marry me?"

Little Lamb

"Baa! Baa!" says Lamb to Mummy Sheep,
"Please can we play hide-and-seek?"

"Where's my lamb?" asks Mummy Sheep.
"Baa! Baa!" shouts Lamb, and out she leaps!

"Baa! Baa!" says Lamb. "I'll hide again –
In the piglets' muddy pen!"

But Mummy finds her right away.
"Baa! Baa!" is all that Lamb can say.

"Baa! Baa!" says Lamb. "I'll hide with my friends."
Mummy says, "There you are with the hens!"

"Baa! Baa!" says Lamb, when the day is done,
"Playing hide-and-seek is fun!"

Little Calf

"Moo! Moo!" says Calf, one sunny day.
"The meadow's where I like to play!"

When a butterfly lands on little Calf's nose,
He says, "Moo! Moo!" and away it goes!

Calf follows the butterfly, calling, "Moo! Moo!"
He sees woolly Lamb and says, "You come too!"

Just then, little pink Piglet appears,
"Moo! Moo!" says Calf. "We're over here!"

As the butterfly flutters off through the air,
Calf says, "Moo! Moo! It's over there!"

Calf snuggles with Mum when his busy day ends.
He says, "Moo! Moo! I've had fun with my friends!"

Wish Upon a Star

If there was one thing that James wanted more than anything else, it was a new friend. He had just moved to a new area and, although he liked his new house, he **missed** his old friends.

"You'll make some new friends soon enough," his mother told him. But for now, James only had his cat, Pumpkin, for company.

James was building a den in the garden. He had found the perfect spot for it and had made some walls from tree branches. It was fun, but James thought it would be even better fun if he had a **friend** to help him.

One night when the sky was clear, James noticed the most beautiful star shining **brightly** in the sky. James thought that it might be a lucky star, so he made a wish.

"Oh, beautiful star, I wish I could make a new friend," he called up into the night.

The next day, James went

out to play in his garden. He was busy
working on his new den when he heard
a strange noise – thwack! James
looked around, but couldn't see what
was making the strange sound.
Thwack! There it was again.
Then, James felt Pumpkin
rubbing his furry body against
his leg and he bent down to give him a
stroke. Pumpkin meowed loudly and
ran off.

"Hey, Pumpkin!" called James. "Where are you off to?"
He followed his cat, who jumped up onto the garden wall
and began to meow even more loudly. He reached up to lift
Pumpkin down again, and it was then that he found out where
the strange sound had been coming from. Thwack!

As James peeped into the next-door garden, he noticed a
boy batting a ball against the wall.

"Hello," said James. "What are you playing?"

"I'm playing tennis, but it's not much fun on my own,"
replied the boy.

The boy, who was called Ben, asked James if he'd like to
play. James was so happy – his wish had come true! They
played ball all morning and then, after lunch, they set to work
finishing off James's den.

That night, James looked up at the night sky. "Thank you,
star," James whispered into the night... "wherever you are!"

The Special Rose

Princess Jasmine was never happier than when she was in her flower meadow. As she walked through the scented field, she would admire the bright colours and pretty petals of the poppies, cornflowers and wild orchids that grew there. "The world is such a beautiful place," she thought to herself.

One day, Princess Jasmine noticed a **perfect** red rose growing amongst the wild flowers. As it did not belong where it was growing, she picked the special rose and placed it by her bed so that she could admire its velvety petals as she drifted off to sleep.

Princess Jasmine usually slept soundly, but that night she dreamt she walked beyond her pretty flower meadow and down a path that she had never seen before. At the end of it was a tiny cottage where an old woman sat **weeping** her heart out.

The next morning, Princess Jasmine set off for her flower meadow and, when she got there, she looked for the little path. At first she found no trace of it at all, but then she noticed another red rose, just like the one she had picked the day before. She picked this rose too and, as she plucked it from the ground, a path opened up before her very eyes.

Princess Jasmine picked her way carefully along the path and found that, just has she had dreamt, the path led to a little cottage. The door was slightly open and she heard the sound of someone crying from within. Princess Jasmine tiptoed in and found the old woman, weeping.

"Why are you crying so?" asked the princess.

"I am sad because I am all alone," replied the woman. She explained that she loved to grow red roses, but now she was too old to tend them and so they had all died.

"What is the world without beauty?" the old woman asked Princess Jasmine.

"I have the most beautiful flower meadow, just up the path from here," the kind princess told the old woman. "You can visit it any time you like. I go there every day and so you will not be lonely any more."

From then on, the old woman met Princess Jasmine every day, and they admired the wild meadow flowers together. Although Princess Jasmine kept on looking, she never found another special red rose growing there.

A Swishy Fishy Day!

Madison and Ethan were the best of friends. They swam everywhere together and loved to play with the friendly fish.

"Let's go for a chariot ride," said Ethan one day. The water was **calm** and clear, so Madison agreed. Liam the seahorse pulled them along in a shell for a chariot, and the two friends rode around the seabed followed by some friendly fish.

"**Whee!**" squealed Ethan.

"**Go faster!**" called Madison. Liam swam just as fast as he could, pulling the two excited friends along behind him. But he swam so fast that the little fish couldn't keep up.

"**Wait for us,**" they called, but Liam sped on and on.

When Liam finally stopped, Ethan and Madison clambered out of the chariot to explore.

But after a while, the sea began to grow rougher and the

water became cloudy. Madison and Ethan climbed back into the chariot and Liam set off for home.

But, oh dear! Where was home? Liam had been swimming so fast he couldn't remember which way they had come, and now the water was so murky he couldn't see which way to go.

"We're lost," cried Madison. "How will we get home?"

"Don't worry," said Ethan, trying his best to comfort his friend. But he was worried too.

They came to a big rock that Ethan thought he recognised, but Madison wasn't so sure.

"It's no good," she sobbed. "We were going so fast I can't remember which rocks we passed on the way."

Just then, some little bubbles floated out of a hole in the rock, and out swam their little fishy friends.

"There you are!" said the smallest red fish. "We couldn't keep up with you so we stopped to take a rest in this rock."

"Do you know the way back?" asked Liam.

"Yes, follow us!" called the fish as they swam home.

When Ethan and Madison got home, they thanked the fish and gave Liam a big hug.

"Next time we go out," said Liam, "let's pay more attention to where we are."

Ethan and Madison happily agreed. They hadn't liked being lost one bit!

The Enormous Turnip

Once upon a time there was an old man who loved to grow vegetables. The old man had some turnip seeds, which he planted in his garden.

Every day the old man watered his seeds. All the turnips began to grow. But one turnip began to grow more than the others. The turnip got bigger and bigger and **bigger** still!

Every day the turnip grew some more. Soon it was the biggest turnip he had ever seen. The old man was very excited.

"Look at my **enormous** turnip," he said to his wife. "I can't wait to eat it!"

One day the old man said, "Today's the day! It's time to pull up my enormous turnip." So the old man pulled as hard as he could. But he **couldn't** pull up the enormous turnip. So the old man called to his wife, "Can you help me pull up my enormous turnip?" So the old woman pulled the old man.

They
pulled
as hard as
they could,
but the enormous
turnip wouldn't even budge.

So the old man said to a
boy, "Can you help me pull up my enormous turnip?"

So the boy pulled the old woman and the old woman pulled
the old man. They all pulled and pulled, but they couldn't pull
up the enormous turnip.

So the old man said to a girl, "Can you help me pull up my
enormous turnip? So the girl pulled the boy, the boy pulled the
old woman and the old woman pulled the old man.

But they couldn't pull up the enormous turnip. So the old
man said to his donkey and his goat, "Can you help me pull
up my enormous turnip?" So the donkey and the goat pulled
the girl who pulled the boy who pulled the old woman who
pulled the old man. They pulled and they pulled and they
pulled and… out came the enormous turnip with a pop!

The old man was very happy. "Look at my enormous
turnip," he said. "Now we can eat turnip for tea."

So the goat and the donkey and the girl and the boy and the
old woman and the old man all had turnip for tea.

And it was the most delicious turnip that any of them
had ever tasted!

Hurt No Living Thing

Hurt no living thing:
Ladybird, nor butterfly,
Nor moth with dusty wing,
Nor cricket chirping cheerily,
Nor grasshopper so light of leap,
Nor dancing gnat, nor beetle fat,
Nor harmless worms that creep.

The Great Brown Owl

The brown owl sits in the ivy-bush,
And she looketh wondrous wise,
With a horny beak beneath her cowl,
And a pair of large, round eyes.

She sat all day on the selfsame spray,
From sunrise till sunset;
And the dim grey light, it was all too bright
For the owl to see in yet.

"Jenny Owlet, Jenny Owlet," said a merry little bird,
"They say you're wondrous wise;
But I don't think you see, though you're looking at me
With your large, round, shining eyes."

But night came soon, and the pale white moon
Rolled high up in the skies;
And the great brown owl flew away in her cowl,
With her large, round, shining eyes.

The Little Doll

I once had a sweet little doll, dears,
The prettiest doll in the world;
Her cheeks were so red and white, dears,
And her hair was so charmingly curled.
But I lost my poor little doll, dears,
As I played in the heath one day;
And I cried for her more than a week, dears,
But I never could find where she lay.

I found my poor little doll, dears,
As I played in the heath one day;
Folks say she is terribly changed, dears,
For her paint is all washed away,
And her arms trodden off by the cows, dears,
And her hair not the least bit curled;
Yet for old sakes' sake, she is still, dears,
The prettiest doll in the world.

Skipping

Little children skip,
The rope so gaily gripping,
Tom and Harry,
Jane and Mary,
Kate, Diana,
Susan, Anna,
All are fond of skipping!

The little boats they skip,
Beside the heavy shipping,
And while the squalling
Winds are calling,
Falling, rising,
Rising, falling,
All are fond of skipping!

The autumn leaves they skip,
When blasts the trees are stripping;
Bounding, whirling,
Sweeping, twirling,
And in wanton
Mazes curling,
All are fond of skipping!

Serena's Lucky Find

Serena the mermaid was sitting on a rock one day, combing her long dark hair, when her friend Sheldon the turtle popped his head out of the water.

"Please will you come for a swim with me, Serena?" asked Sheldon. "The water is so calm and clear today, there will be lots of lovely things to see." So Serena slipped down off the rock and into the water with a splash!

As the two friends swam along, they saw beautiful coral and colourful seaweed, gently swaying in the soft current.

"You're right, Sheldon," said Serena happily, "there are lots of lovely things to see today."

As they swam along further, they met Mrs Clownfish. She looked very worried.

"I've lost my four little babies," she sobbed. "Please help me find them."

Serena and Sheldon swam off to search for the baby fish.

"Don't worry," they called behind them. "We'll soon find them in this lovely clear water." As Serena and Sheldon swam on, they saw something glinting brightly in the water ahead.

"I wonder what that can be?" said Serena, swimming towards the shimmering water ahead. "It's treasure!" she called out to Sheldon, who was paddling as fast as he could to catch up with her.

Sheldon and Serena gasped in amazement at all the beautiful treasure that was spilling out of an old wooden chest. There were rubies, pearls and many other colourful jewels. The two friends picked up pieces of treasure to admire them, and to try on the lovely pieces of jewellery. Then Serena heard a strange sound coming from the treasure chest. Tap! Tap! Tap! It seemed to be coming from inside a large golden locket.

Feeling a little bit nervous, Serena carefully prised open the locket – and out swam the four little baby fish!

"There you are!" exclaimed Serena. "Your mummy has been worried about you!" The little fish swam back behind Sheldon and Serena.

Mrs Clownfish was so happy to see her babies.

"We had a lucky find!" laughed Serena.

"Come here, my little treasures," said Mrs Clownfish, as she gave each of her little fish a lovely hug.

The Princess and the Pea

Once upon a time there was a lonely prince.

"You should find yourself a princess to marry," said his
mother, the queen. But the prince didn't want to
marry just anyone.

"I will only marry a real princess," he said.
The prince had met many beautiful girls. They
wore golden crowns and fine jewels, but they
were not real princesses.

That night, during a thunderstorm, there
was a knock at the door. The prince opened the
door and there stood a girl.

"I am a princess," she said.

The prince liked the girl, but wanted to be sure
that she was a real princess.

"I will find out if this girl is a real princess or not," said the
queen. The queen got a hard dried pea, and she made a bed
for the princess that was twenty mattresses and twenty quilts
high.

"This is your bed," the queen said to the princess. The
princess had never seen such a high bed before, but she climbed
up into it.

"Good night," said the princess. She tried to snuggle down

and go to sleep, but she felt very uncomfortable and was awake all night.

"Did you sleep well?" asked the queen the next morning.

"No, I was awake all night," said the princess. "There was something hard in the bed."

"Only a real princess could feel a pea under so many mattresses," said the queen.

The prince and the real princess were married, and they lived happily ever after.

Benji's New Friends

Benji the bear sat on the end of the bed, feeling a little bit lonely. He was new here and he hadn't seen anyone else in the bedroom.

He watched a moonbeam slip through a gap in the curtains and slide across the bed.

"I wish that I had someone to play with," he whispered.

"Did I hear someone say they wanted to play?" asked a voice. The lid of the toy box flew open, and out climbed a dangly legged, spotty horse.

"Hi, I'm Cleo… and I love to play!"

Boing! Boing!

Cleo jumped onto the bed and began to bounce up and down.

"Where did you come from?" she asked.

"From the birthday party," replied Benji. "I was a present."

"Did someone mention a party?" A friendly looking monkey poked his head around the curtain. "Why weren't Rosie and I invited?"

A floppy-eared rabbit appeared beside him.

"Max and I love parties!" Rosie the rabbit told Benji. "And so does Humph."

"Who's Humph?" asked Benji.

A loud yawn came from inside a box. Then a bright-blue hippo slowly lifted his head.

"I am!" he said. "A party..." he continued thoughtfully. "That means food. And I'm hungry! Is there anything left to eat?"

"I think there are some cakes in the kitchen," replied Benji, "but do you think we should...?"

But Humph was already through the door!

"Oh!" said Benji, looking at the other toys. "Should we go after him?"

Benji was bumping down the stairs after Humph when Cleo zoomed past.

"This is fun!" she neighed.

"Wait for me!" called Benji.

In the kitchen, Humph was about to take a bite out of a leftover cupcake with a candle in it.

The candle was already halfway into Humph's mouth. Benji grabbed it just in time.

"Excuse me," he explained, "but you aren't meant to eat that bit."

"Thanks, Benji. You're smart. I wish I knew things like that," grumbled Humph.

Before Benji could explain about the candle, he heard Rosie yell loudly. Benji raced back up to the bedroom where he found Rosie hiding under the bed. She had seen a big owl swoop past the window and it had given her quite a fright.

"Don't worry," said Benji, and he explained to everyone that owls never came inside people's houses and that they were all quite safe.

"Benji, will you always be here to look after us?" Cleo asked him. Benji gave a tiny little smile. It was nice to feel wanted. "Of course," he replied.

Humph was tired from their adventure. "How am I going to sleep when I'm so hungry?" he sniffed, settling back down on the bed.

Cleo and Rosie giggled. They danced around on the bed. Max joined in.

"Why don't we all play in the garden tomorrow?" Rosie suggested.

"What's your garden like?" asked Benji.

"I'll show you," said Cleo, and she helped Benji up to have a look out of the window.

"Wow!" he said. "It looks really exciting. Are you going to play in the garden, Humph?"

"Humph!" said Humph sleepily. "It's such a long way to the garden. I might just have a little nap instead."

Benji smiled at his new sleepy friend.

Cleo jumped back onto the bed and started to bounce. Benji looked up at the moon. He had a feeling that he wouldn't be lonely any more.

"I wish that tomorrow will be as much fun as today," he whispered.

Then Benji turned to his new friends, took a huge leap, and began to bounce on the bed.

"Here's to friends!" he laughed.

The Seasons

In the winter comes the snow,
Makes our feet and fingers glow.
Early spring brings the rain,
Thaws the frozen ponds again.
Then come breezes, loud and shrill,
They stir the dancing daffodil.
Soon flowers the primrose sweet,
Daisies scatter at our feet.
See the flocks of pretty lambs,
Skipping by their fleecy dams!
Summer brings tulips, lilies, roses;
Fills the children's hands and posies.
Then it brings us cooling showers,
Strawberries and gilly-flowers.
The sun ripens sheaves of corn,
Then the harvest home is borne.
In the autumn comes the pheasant;
Then to gather nuts is pleasant.
But all too soon come icy blasts,
Then the leaves are falling fast.
In the winter comes the snow,
Makes our feet and fingers glow.

The Moon

The moon has a face like the clock in the hall;
She shines on thieves on the garden wall,
On streets and fields and harbour quays,
And birdies asleep in the forks of the trees.

The squalling cat and the squeaking mouse,
The howling dog by the door of the house,
The bat that lies in bed at noon,
All love to be out by the light of the moon.

But all of the things that belong to the day
Cuddle to sleep to be out of her way;
And flowers and children close their eyes
Till up in the morning the sun shall arise.

Bed in Summer

In winter I get up at night,
And dress by yellow candle-light.
In summer, quite the other way,
I have to go to bed by day.

Bedtime

The evening is coming; the sun sinks to rest,
The rooks are all flying straight home to nest.
"Caw!" says the rook, as he flies overhead;
"It's time little people were going to bed!"

The Owl

When cats run home and light is come,
And dew is cold upon the ground,
And the far-off stream is dumb
And the whirring sail goes round;
Alone and warming his five wits,
The white owl in the belfry sits.

The Wise Old Owl

There was an old owl who lived in an oak;
The more he heard the less he spoke.
The less he spoke, the more he heard.
Why aren't we like that wise old bird?

Hush, Little Baby

Hush, little baby, don't say a word,
Papa's gonna buy you a mockingbird.

If that mocking bird don't sing,
Papa's gonna buy you a diamond ring.

If that diamond ring turns brass,
Papa's gonna buy you a looking glass.

If that looking glass gets broke,
Papa's gonna buy you a billy goat.

If that billy goat don't pull,
Papa's gonna buy you a cart and bull.

If that cart and bull turn over,
Papa's gonna buy you a dog named Rover.

And if that dog named Rover won't bark.
Papa's gonna to buy you and horse and cart.

And if that horse and cart fall down,
You'll still be the sweetest little baby in town.

Chicken Licken

One day, Chicken Licken was in the woods when, BOINK!
an acorn fell onto her head.

"Ruffle my feathers!" said Chicken Licken.
"The sky is falling down. I must tell the
king at once." And off she ran.

On her way, Chicken Licken met Cocky Locky
who was on her way to the woods.

"Oh, don't go!" clucked Chicken Licken. "I was
there a moment ago, and the sky fell on my head!
I'm off to tell the king right away, you can come
with me." And off they hurried.

Soon they met Ducky Lucky on his way for a swim in the
pond.

"Oh, stop, Ducky Lucky!" squawked Chicken Licken. "The
sky in the woods is falling down! We're off to tell the king at
once, you can come with us."

They had just set off again, when Ducky Lucky
saw Goosey Loosey.

"Oh, Goosey Loosey," he quacked, "the sky
in the woods is falling down. We have to
tell the king right away! You can come
with us."

So the four birds went along, until
they met Foxy Loxy.

"Good day to you all!" said the

crafty fox. "Where are you going this fine day?"

"We're off to see the king," announced Chicken Licken. "The sky fell on my head in the woods. We must tell him at once."

Foxy Loxy grinned slyly. "I can show you a short cut," he said, leading the way.

So the four birds followed Foxy Loxy, until they came to a narrow, dark hole in the hillside.

"This way!" said sly Foxy Loxy. He led Cocky Locky, Ducky Lucky and Goosey Loosey into his den. Chicken Licken was about to follow when… all of a sudden, Goosey Loosey let out a loud "Honk!" Then Ducky Lucky let out a shrill "Quack!" and Cocky Locky cried out, "Cock-a-doodle-do!"

"Foxy Loxy has eaten Goosey Loosey, Ducky Lucky and Cocky Locky," cried Chicken Licken. "I must run away!"

Chicken Licken ran all the way home without stopping. And she never did tell the king that the sky was falling down.

The Lucky Shoes

Today was a very special day. Sophie and Gemma were going to perform in their first ever ballet concert. All of their friends and family would be in the audience watching them dance.

"I hope we don't make any mistakes," said Sophie, who was feeling nervous.

"I'll be wearing my lucky ballet shoes," said Gemma, "and they haven't let me down yet!"

The two friends walked to the concert together. They **skipped** happily through the park, twirling and leaping as they went. It was a hot day and, as they had plenty of time, they stopped for a while to catch their breath and drink some water.

"Phew, I'm so hot," gasped Gemma. "I think I'll take off my shoes for a while." As the two girls sat there resting and chatting, they didn't notice a little puppy sneaking up on them and running off with Gemma's lucky shoes. When Sophie and Gemma got up to go, Gemma couldn't find her shoes anywhere.

"My lucky shoes!" she gasped. "Where are they?"

Sophie and Gemma searched beneath bushes and under trees, but there was no trace of Gemma's lucky shoes.

Meanwhile, another little dancer was also making her way through the park to the ballet concert. She saw Gemma's lucky shoes on the path where the puppy had dropped them, and picked them up.

"Oh! What lovely shoes. Somebody must have dropped them," she thought. And wondering if they would fit her, she took her own shoes off to try them on. But the little dancer's head was so full of dreams about dancing in the lovely shoes, that she didn't notice the little puppy bound out from behind some bushes and run away with her shoes – and Gemma's lucky shoes as well! The little dancer was sitting on the path feeling very puzzled when Sophie ran up to her.

"Oh, hello," she said. "Have you seen a lovely pair of ballet shoes anywhere? They belong to my friend Gemma and they're her lucky shoes. They just disappeared!"

"Yes," replied the little dancer. "They were right here, but now they've gone. My own shoes have vanished, too!"

"How strange!" said

Sophie, scratching her head.

While Sophie and Gemma continued to search for the lucky shoes, the cheeky little puppy was having a lovely time scampering around the park. After a while, the puppy saw a fountain and went to take a drink from it, dropping Gemma's special shoes onto the floor.

Before long, another little girl came along and found the dainty ballet shoes.

"How pretty!" exclaimed the girl as she put them on and danced around the fountain. Feeling very lucky to have found such pretty shoes, she was about to run off to show her mother. But just then, Sophie and Gemma's friend, Jessica, happened to come past, also on her way to the concert. She saw the little girl dancing around and recognised Gemma's special shoes right away.

"Excuse me," she said to the little girl, "but are those your shoes? They look just like a pair that belong to my friend Gemma."

"No," replied the girl, "they're not mine. I just found them on the floor." The little girl took the shoes off and gave them to Jessica.

"They are lovely shoes," she said. "I hope your friend won't mind that I tried them on."

"I'm sure she'll be so pleased to get them back that she won't mind at all," said Jessica. "I'm just going to watch her dance in a concert. Perhaps you'd like to come and see her dance, too."

"Oh, yes," replied the girl, and she ran off to ask her mum.

The two girls went off to the concert together, and on the way they met Sophie and Gemma. They had found the ballet shoes belonging to the other little dancer, but were still searching for Gemma's lucky shoes.

"My lucky shoes!" cried Gemma when she saw what Jessica was carrying. "Thank goodness you found them."

They all hurried off to the concert hall and got there just in time for Sophie and Gemma to change for the performance.

Gemma and Sophie both danced beautifully, without making a single mistake.

As Gemma and Sophie took their final bow, the sound of rapturous applause rang in their ears.

"Your shoes really are lucky," smiled Sophie. "They went dancing all around the park this morning, but they still found their way back to you!"

"Yes," replied Gemma. "I always knew these shoes were rather special. I'll never let them out of my sight again!"

The Little Mermaid

Deep beneath the ocean, in a magical watery world, there lived a little mermaid. Although she was very happy under the sea, the little mermaid loved to explore and often swam to the surface, even though her father had told her not to.

One stormy day, the little mermaid swam up to watch the waves splashing against the rocks. She loved the thundery grey clouds and the fresh drops of rainwater that fell upon her face. As she watched from behind a rock, she noticed a ship that was struggling to stay afloat in the stormy waters. Whoosh! A huge wave hit the ship and sent it crashing against the rocks. The little mermaid watched helplessly as the fine vessel began to sink.

As the passengers and crew scrambled into the life boats, the little mermaid noticed one very handsome man who was unconscious in the water. Although it was forbidden to be seen by humans, she swam over to him and took him safely to the shore. As the little mermaid waited for the young man to recover, she sang him a beautiful melody. Before long he began to wake up and, as soon as their eyes met, they fell in love.

When the mermaid heard the sound of human voices approaching, she hid behind a rock and watched as some men rushed over to the young man's side.

"Your majesty, thank goodness you're safe," they said. And it was then that the little mermaid realised that her handsome young man was a prince.

Safely back under the sea, the little mermaid could not stop thinking about the prince and she knew she just had to find a way of seeing him again.

In the murky depths, amongst the darkest caves, there lived a sea witch. The little mermaid knew in her heart that the witch was evil, but she wanted to see her prince again so badly that she paid her a visit.

"Poor little heartbroken mermaid," the witch cackled. "I will give you human legs so that you can see your precious prince, but in return I will take your lovely voice! Ha, ha, ha, ha!"

The little mermaid accepted. She would have given anything to be with her true love. Surely he would recognise her, even if she was unable to tell him who she was.

And so the little mermaid swam to the surface, leaving her beautiful voice behind. She collapsed, exhausted, onto the same beach where she had last seen the prince. As luck would have it, the prince was walking on the beach and found her. But although he thought she looked familiar, the prince did not recognise her as the mysterious girl who had saved his life.

"Who are you?" he asked her, but the little mermaid had no words to tell him.

The prince took pity on the strange girl and thought perhaps she might be a survivor from a shipwreck. Although she could not speak, he found her to be a wonderful companion, and grew fonder of her each day.

The little mermaid was happy to be with her prince and thought that he was sure to remember her one day – it would just take time.

But the wicked sea witch was spying on the little mermaid and had become very jealous. It was not enough for her that she had the mermaid's beautiful voice, she wanted the prince for herself, too. She transformed herself into a beautiful woman and set off to meet the prince.

"I am the woman who saved your life," she told the prince, and she entranced him by using the little mermaid's pure young voice, which she kept in a glass bottle around her neck. The prince believed the witch was the girl who had saved him, and he asked her to marry him.

As the palace prepared for a royal wedding, the little mermaid wept bitter tears.

"My heart will break!" she thought to herself as she sobbed.

The day of the wedding arrived and the little mermaid watched on helplessly as the disguised witch walked down the aisle. As she passed the little mermaid she gave her an evil smirk, and was enjoying herself so much that she forgot to watch her step. The witch tripped over her wedding gown and fell. She landed on the bottle, smashing it to smithereens. The mermaid's voice broke free and returned to her.

At once the little mermaid began to sing the same beautiful melody that she had sung on the day she had rescued the prince. The sea witch's magic spell was broken and the prince came to his senses. The sea witch vanished in a puff of smoke and the prince was free to marry his true love. They both lived happily ever after.

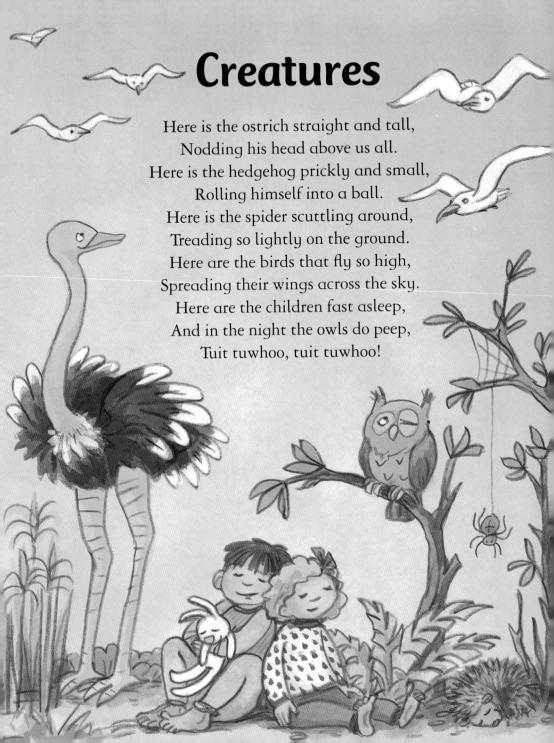

Creatures

Here is the ostrich straight and tall,
Nodding his head above us all.
Here is the hedgehog prickly and small,
Rolling himself into a ball.
Here is the spider scuttling around,
Treading so lightly on the ground.
Here are the birds that fly so high,
Spreading their wings across the sky.
Here are the children fast asleep,
And in the night the owls do peep,
Tuit tuwhoo, tuit tuwhoo!

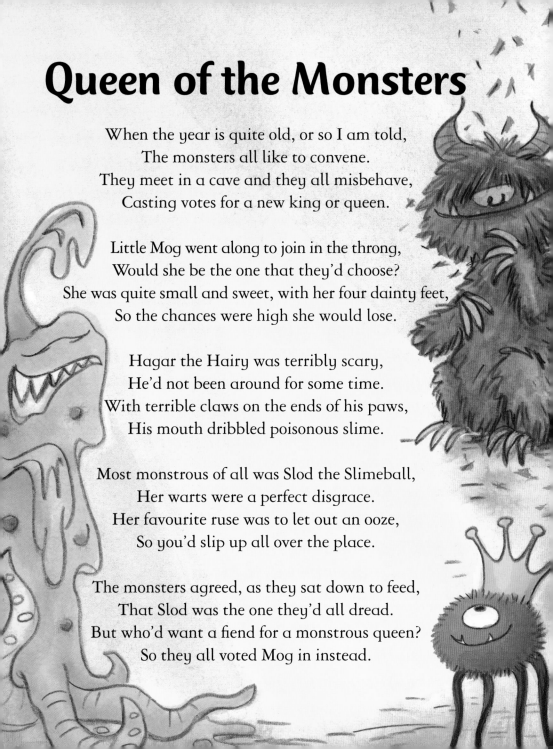

Queen of the Monsters

When the year is quite old, or so I am told,
The monsters all like to convene.
They meet in a cave and they all misbehave,
Casting votes for a new king or queen.

Little Mog went along to join in the throng,
Would she be the one that they'd choose?
She was quite small and sweet, with her four dainty feet,
So the chances were high she would lose.

Hagar the Hairy was terribly scary,
He'd not been around for some time.
With terrible claws on the ends of his paws,
His mouth dribbled poisonous slime.

Most monstrous of all was Slod the Slimeball,
Her warts were a perfect disgrace.
Her favourite ruse was to let out an ooze,
So you'd slip up all over the place.

The monsters agreed, as they sat down to feed,
That Slod was the one they'd all dread.
But who'd want a fiend for a monstrous queen?
So they all voted Mog in instead.

As I Was Going to St Ives

As I was going to St Ives,
I met a man with seven wives.
Each wife had seven sacks,
Each sack had seven cats,
Each cat had seven kits.
Kits, cats, sacks and wives,
How many were going to St Ives?

I Saw Three Ships

I saw three ships come sailing by,
Come sailing by, come sailing by;
I saw three ships come sailing by,
On New Year's Day in the morning.

And what do you think was in them then,
Was in them then, was in them then?
And what do you think was in them then,
On New Year's Day in the morning?

Three pretty girls were in them then,
Were in them then, were in them then;
Three pretty girls were in them then,
On New Year's Day in the morning.

And one could whistle, and one could sing,
And one could play on the violin –
Such joy there was at my wedding,
On New Year's Day in the morning.

The Three Billy Goats Gruff

Once upon a time, there were three Billy Goats Gruff. There was a little billy goat with little horns. There was a middle-sized billy goat with middle-sized horns. And there was a big billy goat with very big horns.

The three billy goats lived in a field and they ate grass all day long. A river ran through the field and over it stood a bridge. Beneath the bridge lived a big, bad, ugly troll.

One day, the little billy goat looked at the field over the bridge. The grass looked long and juicy. He wanted to eat that grass. So the brave little billy goat went onto the bridge with a **trip trap, trip trap.** But the bad troll jumped out.

"I'm going to eat you!" he said.

"No, you can't eat me!" said the little billy goat. "I'm just a little goat. Wait for the middle-sized goat and eat him. He will be far more tasty."

So the bad troll did just that. Then the middle-sized billy goat looked at the field over the bridge. The grass looked long and juicy. He wanted to eat that grass.

So the middle-sized billy goat went onto the bridge with a

clip clop, clip clop. But the bad troll jumped out.

"I'm going to eat you!" he said.

"No, you can't eat me!" said the middle-sized billy goat.

"I'm just a middle-sized goat. Wait for the big goat and eat him." So the bad troll did just that.

Then the big billy goat looked at the field over the bridge. The grass looked long and juicy. He wanted to eat that grass.

So the big billy goat went onto the bridge with a thump, thump, thump, thump. But the bad troll jumped out.

"I'm going to eat you!" he said.

"No, you can't eat me," said the big billy goat. "I'm a big goat and I have very big horns. I will toss you into the air with my big horns." He put his head down and ran at the bad troll. He tossed him high up into the air. Then the bad troll fell into the river. And that was the end of him!

The Magic Sea Shell

Once upon a time, there was a fisherman's daughter named Marina. On the days when her father was out at sea, Marina would wait for him on the beach and search for pretty shells to add to her collection.

On one such day, a storm began to blow in. As the sea grew rougher, Marina began to worry about her father.

Marina waited and watched, but there was no sign of her father's little fishing boat. As she waited, she saw other boats come in. "Have you seen my father's boat?" Marina asked them, but nobody had.

Marina was beginning to despair when she noticed a beautiful pink shell on the sands, shimmering more brightly than any she had ever seen. She picked it up, put it to her ear and heard a tiny voice:

"Out beyond the bay, sticking up above the waves, a man clings to a rock, waiting to be saved."

Marina ran for help and a brave crew of men set off to find her father. They sailed out into the stormy sea and, sure enough, just as the shell had said, they found Marina's father clinging onto a rock for dear life.

Marina never heard the shell's voice again, but she kept the shell and gave it pride of place in her collection.

The Goose-Girl

A princess, who was to marry a prince, set off on a journey to her wedding day with her maid. She took precious gifts for her new husband, and wore fine clothes for the wedding.

The maid, however, was an evil girl. She made the princess swap clothes with her and give her all the treasures.

When they arrived at the palace, the prince mistook the maid for his bride and the princess for a maid.

"Put my maid to work with the geese," said the wicked imposter.

But the old king could not help but notice how beautiful the new goose-girl was, and asked her where she had come from. The poor girl didn't tell the king, for she had promised not to tell a soul.

"If you can't tell me, then tell the stove," said the wise old king, and he left the room and hid by the boiler pipe where he could hear her. The real princess sobbed as she told the stove the truth about who she was. The old king heard everything.

The wicked maid was banished, and the true princess married her prince and lived happily ever after.

The Tortoise and the Hare

Once upon a time, there was a hare who was always boasting about how fast he was.

"I," he would say, puffing out his chest and flexing his legs, "am the speediest animal in the forest. I have never been beaten. I challenge anyone to try to beat me."

And, of course, nobody took up the challenge because he was right – he was the fastest animal in the forest.

The animals who lived in the forest were becoming tired of Hare's bragging. Until one day, much to everyone's surprise, after Hare had been boasting even more than normal...

"Okay, Hare. I'll race you," Tortoise said.

"Whaaaaat?" laughed Hare. "You've got to be joking. Tortoise, you're the slowest animal in the forest. I'll run circles around you."

"You might be fast," replied Tortoise, "but speed isn't everything. Why don't we have a race? You can

keep your boasting until you actually beat me."

"Speed might not be everything but it sure helps in a race," laughed Hare. He laughed so much that he fell to his knees and thumped the floor with his fist. He'd never heard of anything so ridiculous in his life.

That night, while the forest animals prepared the course, Tortoise went to bed early so he'd have a lot of energy for the race. Hare, meanwhile, stayed up late boxing with his friends. He knew he could beat the slow tortoise even if he was tired.

There was a buzz of excitement in the forest the next morning. No one had heard of Hare ever losing a race so this was going to be quite an event to watch! Everyone gathered at the starting line to watch the race begin. All the forest animals wanted Tortoise to win, but deep down they knew that Hare was the fastest.

Tortoise was already at the starting line, trying his best to look confident. He looked around for Hare, who had just arrived and was making his way to the starting line. He strutted towards Tortoise with his chest puffed out proudly. The crowd fell silent…

"On your marks, get set…GO!" cried the starting fox.

And Hare flew off at high speed, leaving a cloud of dust where he had just stood. The tortoise trudged behind much, much, much more slooooooowly.

Hare decided to take a quick look behind to see where the slow tortoise was. When he saw that Tortoise was far, far away, he decided to stop for breakfast. He feasted on some juicy carrots. Then he lay on his back, fiddled with his ears, and yawned.

"This is just too easy," he said, loud enough for just about all the animals in the forest to hear. "I think I'll have forty winks and catch up with him later." Soon he was snoring happily away. ZZZZZZZ!

Tortoise got to where Hare was lying, fast asleep. "Maybe I should wake him?" he thought, as he plodded past Hare. "No, I'm sure Hare wouldn't like that. He will wake up soon enough and come whizzing by."

And so Tortoise plodded on and on and on. Hare slept, on and on and on. In Hare's dreams, all the forest animals cheered and clapped as he streamed past the finish line.

The sun began to sink, and still Tortoise plodded on, and still Hare slept. The sun was just about to set when Hare awoke with a jolt.

He could just see Tortoise in the distance, plodding slowly

and carefully towards the finish line.

"Noooooooo!" cried Hare. He leapt to his feet and charged towards the finish.

He ran as fast as his legs could carry him, but it just wasn't fast enough – **he was too late!**

Tortoise was over the line before him. Hare had been beaten fair and square.

Tortoise was a hero, and all the forest animals were there to cheer him.

After that, if anyone heard Hare **boasting** about how fast he could run, they reminded him about the day that Tortoise had beaten him.

"Slow and steady won the race," they would say.

And all Hare could do was smile and shrug because, after all, they were absolutely right.

Rosie and Bluebell

Rosie and Bluebell went out one day,
Gathering flowers they found on their way.
Petals of yellow, purple and pink,
Bunched up together as quick as a wink.

"Mine are for Mummy," said Bluebell to Rosie,
"She'll be so pleased with this lovely posy."
"Mine are for Grandma," said Rosie to Bluebell,
"She will so love the nice way that they smell."

Bluebell and Rosie skipped home happily,
Holding the posies they'd picked with such glee.
"Hello!" they called as they ran through the door,
Clutching their handfuls of petals galore.

"Thank you so much!" said Grandma to Rosie,
As she handed over her beautiful posy.
"Gorgeous!" said Mummy, hugging Bluebell,
"What a truly beautiful smell!"

The Moonlit Moors

The heat has lifted from the land,
The dusky light is dim.
The moon is rising in the sky;
The night is moving in.

Rabbits raise their timid heads
Above the moonlit moors,
They sniff the air and wonder
If it's safe to go outdoors.

The heather glows so softly
In the silvery twilight,
Beautiful, beneath the moon
Which shines its gentle light.

There's no place I'd rather be
At this special time,
For when the moon is on the moors,
I feel the world is mine.

My Birthday Wish

I have a special secret wish,
One I cannot share.
I'll lock it up inside my heart;
It will be safe in there.

Nobody must find out what
Is under lock and key.
So please don't try to take a peek,
There's nothing you can see.

I'll keep it 'til my birthday,
Then I'll open up and take
My secret from its hiding place –
And wish upon my cake!

Sail Away

Sail away, for a year and a day,
To a land where dreams come true,
Lit by the moon and a blanket of stars,
Across the ocean blue.

We'll drift through silver waters
To lands we've never seen
In daylight hours, where chocolate flowers
Will taste just like a dream.

Where clouds are cotton candy,
And the sky is always blue.
What busy night-time travelling,
Will you come with us, too?

Puss in Boots

There was once an old miller who died, leaving his mill to his eldest son, his donkey to his middle son and his cat to his youngest son, who was called Jack. Jack was so poor that he could barely afford to feed himself, let alone the poor creature as well.

"What am I going to do with you?" Jack asked the cat.

Although he spoke to the cat, he certainly didn't expect an answer, so you can imagine his surprise when the cat said:

"Don't worry about a thing. Just give me a pair of boots, a hat and a sack and you'll soon discover what I'm worth."

Jack quickly saw that this was no ordinary puss, so with his last coins, he gave the cat what he wanted.

The cat looked so funny all dressed up that Jack laughed until his sides hurt. He decided to call him Puss in Boots.

The following morning Puss in Boots went hunting and immediately caught a fine rabbit. He set off to the king's palace with the rabbit in his sack. At the palace, he presented it to the king and said:

"This is a gift from my master, the Marquis of Carabas." (This was a name that he had just made up).

The king was delighted with the gift. "Perhaps I could call

on your master and thank him myself," he suggested.

Puss in Boots gave the king directions to his master's castle. The king promised he would call the next day, and bring his beautiful daughter, Melissa, with him.

The next morning, Puss in Boots took Jack to a lake on the road that he had told the king his master's castle was on. He told his master to get in the water, and as soon as Jack dived in, Puss in Boots hid his clothes and ran to meet the king.

"Help, help!" cried Puss, as soon as he spotted the king's carriage. "Robbers have stolen my master's clothes."

The king gave some spare clothes to Jack, who quickly got dressed. The king invited Jack to join him and Princess Melissa in the royal carriage. Jack looked so handsome that the princess fell in love with him on the spot.

Once they were all safely in the carriage, Puss in Boots raced ahead. He came to a field where some men were working.

"When the king comes passing by, you must tell him that these fields belong to the

Marquis of Carabas. If you don't, it'll be off with your heads!" he told the men.

Sure enough, when the king passed the field of workers he stopped and asked who owned the land.

"Why, the Marquis of Carabas, Your Majesty," they all replied, for no one wanted to lose their head. The king was impressed, even though poor Jack looked a little confused.

As it happened, the fields and lands really belonged to a fierce giant who lived in a castle at the end of the road. Puss in Boots hurried to the castle and knocked on the door.

"WHO GOES THERE?" roared the giant.

"Just me," replied Puss in Boots. "I've travelled from far away because I've heard that you are a wonderful magician. I have heard that you can change yourself into any animal you want."

"True," said the giant, who was very vain and a bit of a show-off. Then he turned himself into a huge lion.

"That's very impressive," said Puss in Boots. "But I bet a huge fellow like you couldn't turn yourself into something small, such as... a teeny-tiny mouse!"

"Easy-peasy," boasted the giant, immediately turning himself into a little brown mouse. In a flash, the cunning puss pounced on the mouse and gobbled him up.

Just then, the king's carriage arrived at the castle. Puss in Boots raced out to welcome him.

"Welcome to the Marquis of Carabas's humble home," said the cat, with a sweeping bow.

"You mean to say that this is all yours?" said the king, turning to Jack. At first Jack looked confused, but when Puss in Boots winked at him, he held out his hand and led Princess Melissa into the castle.

The king was so impressed that when Jack, or the Marquis of Carabas as he was now called, asked him for his daughter's hand in marriage, he quickly agreed.

Indeed, he heartily congratulated himself on finding such a fine son-in-law. And from that day forth, the Marquis of Carabas, the princess, and, of course, Puss in Boots lived happily ever after.

Party Time in Twinkle Town

The fairies of Twinkle Town were excited because they were expecting a very special visitor. Only the town's chief fairy knew who was coming, and she was keeping it a closely guarded secret.

"You'll just have to wait and see," she teased, when the little fairies begged her to tell them.

Everyone was hard at work using their magic to clean and tidy. Even the flowers were getting a dust and a polish!

Soon everything was ready for the surprise visitor, and the fairies of Twinkle Town didn't have to wait long before they heard a **magical tinkling sound** getting louder and

louder, and a beautiful pink mist getting closer and closer. Finally, there was a gentle explosion of lights and colour, and then their eyes met with a wonderful sight...

It was the Fairy Queen!

Everyone clapped and cheered.

The Fairy Queen admired Twinkle Town and declared it the cleanest town in Fairyland. The party food was fantastic; the cakes were magic and when you bit into them little birds flew out and began to sing.

The Queen was very impressed. "Goodness me!" she exclaimed. "All this must have taken a lot of hard work and magic."

"Let's have some dancing," suggested the chief fairy. She raised her magic wand to conjure up some fairy dance music... but nothing happened.

"**Whoops!**" she said, blushing slightly. "I'll just try that again." But still nothing happened!

"Oh dear," said the Fairy Queen. "You must have used up all your magic dust getting ready for my party!"

The Fairy Queen waved her own special magic wand and conjured up some music. The dancing went on way into the night, and everyone agreed it was the best party that Twinkle Town had ever had.

Woodland Rescue

Bella loved nature. Whenever she went walking, she always looked out for wildlife and trees.

One day, Bella was strolling through the woods. As she walked along, she could hear the sounds of nature. Chirp! Cheep! There were so many birds singing that it was hard to tell one from another. The different sounds blended together, creating a birdsong orchestra.

Just then, Bella heard something unusual. Scraaaape! It was a scuttling and scraping. No animal that Bella knew of made a sound like that. Standing very still, Bella listened to hear where the sound was coming from. Slowly and quietly, so as not to scare the creature away, she peeped behind the nearest tree and there was a baby squirrel. It was scrambling to get out from a hollow at the bottom of the tree, but it was stuck.

Bella didn't want to frighten the poor creature, but she could see that it needed help. The squirrel had its paw stuck in a plastic drink bottle – so that's what was making the scraping sound!

The baby squirrel was frozen with fear as Bella bent down to release its trapped paw. When the paw was free, it still didn't move.

"Don't be frightened of me little squirrel, I'm here to help you," whispered Bella. But when the squirrel still didn't move, she crept away, back behind the tree, and waited as still as a statue. When the squirrel thought she'd gone, he scampered off to find his mother.

Bella was happy that she had rescued the squirrel, but she felt angry too.

"It's wrong to leave litter in the woods," she thought. And then Bella had a wonderful idea.

That evening, Bella invited her friends round for a sleepover.

"Bring some coloured crayons and pencils," she told them.

When her friends arrived, she told them all about her woodland rescue. Her friends all agreed to help.

Bella's parents were rather puzzled that Bella and her friends were so quiet that evening because sleepovers were usually much noisier than this!

"What are those girls up to?" asked Bella's dad. They soon found out that the girls had been working hard making a big poster to stick up at the entrance to the woods.

Litter Harms Wildlife, the poster read. It was decorated with beautiful pictures of squirrels, foxes, owls and lots of other woodland creatures.

Bella and her friends would make sure that everybody got the message.

Little Bear's Close Encounter

Little Bear looked up at the stars.

"I wish I was an astronaut," he sighed.

Little Bear dreamed of exploring the
world outside the window. He liked living in
Emma's bedroom, but he sometimes wondered
what it would be like to climb a mountain
or go deep-sea diving. Most of all, Little Bear
longed to meet an alien.

"Twinkle, twinkle, little bear," he sang
to himself. "How I wonder what's up there."

"What are you looking at?" asked Monkey, coming over to
join him at the window.

"I'm looking for spaceships," replied Little Bear, pressing
his furry nose up against the window. "I want to meet a real
alien," he explained.

"I wonder what they look like?" said Monkey.

Little Bear told Monkey that Emma had a book all about
aliens that they read together.

"They come in all shapes and sizes," he said.

"Are they scary?" asked Monkey.

"I hope not!" Little Bear replied.

Suddenly a big black shape appeared at the window,
looming over the two friends.

"Aaargh! An alien!" cried Little Bear, jumping down from the windowsill.

"Do aliens meow?" asked Monkey.

"I'm not sure that they do," whispered Little Bear, peeping out from between his paws.

"Do aliens purr?" asked Monkey.

"It didn't say anything about purring in Emma's book," said Little Bear, feeling a little braver.

Do aliens have whiskers and a long furry tail?" giggled Monkey.

"Definitely not!" said Little Bear, beginning to feel rather foolish.

Little Bear and Monkey climbed back onto the windowsill. Was it an alien? No it was Emma's cat, Sooty.

"Meow!" said Sooty.

Little Bear decided that he'd had enough excitement for one night.

"Perhaps I don't want to meet an alien, after all," he chuckled.

Sippity Sup, Sippity Sup

Sippity sup, sippity sup,
Bread and milk from a china cup.
Bread and milk from a bright silver spoon
Made of a piece of the bright silver moon.
Sippity sup, sippity sup,
Sippity, sippity sup.

Vintery, Mintery

Vintery, mintery, cutery, corn,
Apple seed and apple thorn;
Wire, briar, limber lock,
Three geese in a flock.
One flew east, and one flew west,
And one flew over the cuckoo's nest.

It's Raining, It's Pouring

It's raining, it's pouring,
The old man is snoring.
He went to bed and he bumped his head,
And couldn't get up in the morning.

There Was a Crooked Man

There was a crooked man and he walked a crooked mile,
He found a crooked sixpence upon a crooked stile;
He bought a crooked cat,
Which caught a crooked mouse,
And they all lived together in a little crooked house.

Michael Finnegan

There was an old man called Michael Finnegan.
He grew whiskers on his chinnegan.
The wind came out and blew them in again.
Poor old Michael Finnegan.
Begin again.

Diddle, Diddle, Dumpling

Diddle, diddle, dumpling, my son John,
Went to bed with his trousers on;
One shoe off, and one shoe on,
Diddle, diddle, dumpling, my son John.

The River

Moody river, running fast,
Deep and foaming as you pass.
Rain has swelled your water high,
Murky swirls go sweeping by.

Angry now, you froth and churn
The water reeds, which twist and turn.
The ducks all hide beneath their wings,
The wildlife shelters, no birds sing.

Until the torrents heave a sigh,
And clouds are lifting from the sky.
Calm descends, the storm has gone.
The water's still, the sun is strong.

The peaceful river's clear at last.
The sparkling water ambles past
And finds its way quite happily,
Through green fields, then out to sea.

The riverbank's alive and green,
The gurgling water's fresh and clean.
The fish can jump, the ducklings float,
And I can row my rowing boat.

Grumpy Fairy

Misery didn't have any friends. It was her own fault, she was always grumbling. Willow, her niece, couldn't understand

her. "Why do you always find fault with everyone?" she asked.

"Because everybody is so useless!" said her grumpy aunt.

One day Misery told the fairy who baked the bread, "Your bread is too soft. I like crusty bread."

"If that's your attitude," said the baker fairy, "bake your own bread!"

"I shall!" said Misery.

The next day she was rude to the fairy who mended her shoes.

"No one speaks to me like that!" said the cobbler fairy. "From now on you can mend your own shoes."

"I'll be glad to," said Misery grumpily.

Then she insulted the fairy who collected honey from the bees.

"How dare you?" said the honey-collector fairy. "I'm not staying here to be insulted. You can collect your own honey."

"How are you going to manage?" Willow asked Misery.

"No problem," said Misery. "I'll do everything myself." And with that she set to work to bake some bread. Misery mixed and kneaded the dough and left it to rise. Then she put the loaf in the oven, and sat down for a well-earned rest. Soon she had

nodded off.

She was woken by a smell of burning. All that was left of the loaf of bread were a few burnt cinders. What Misery didn't realize was that the baker fairy used a special baking spell – a spell that Misery didn't know!

Misery went to collect some honey. She waved her arms at the bees buzzing round the hive, shouting, "Out of my way, bees." They didn't like it one little bit! Their answer was to swarm around her and sting her. You see, what Misery didn't know was that the honey fairy used a special honey-collecting spell.

Misery ran from the bees as fast as she could. As she did, she broke her shoe! Oh dear! What a state she was in! Burnt bread, bee stings and only one shoe!

"You can't go on like this," said Willow, when she saw Misery.

Misery did some serious thinking. "Tell all the fairies I've turned over a new leaf," she told Willow. "From now on I shan't be grumpy any more."

Willow was delighted! Misery didn't complain about anything for months after that, and Willow kept her fingers crossed that it would last.

Princess Mia and the Big Smile

Princess Mia was a very lively girl. She was always bouncing around and getting into scrapes. Her father wanted her to act more like a princess.

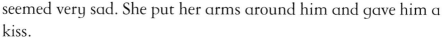

"You must be more serious!" the king told his daughter.

The princess looked at the king's serious face. And then she looked at his down-turned mouth. He looked so serious that he seemed very sad. She put her arms around him and gave him a kiss.

"It's not me who needs to be more serious," she told her dad. "It's you who needs to smile more, Daddy."

Princess Mia showed the king how to dance around the palace gardens and do cartwheels. **Whee!** The king wasn't very good at them but he kept trying again and again.

Suddenly, his face wasn't quite so serious. Princess Mia showed the king how to make a kite swoop through the sky like a bird. **Whoosh!**

The king got his string tangled once or twice, but he did quite well for a beginner.

His face was looking less serious by the minute.

"Well done, Daddy!" cried Princess Mia. The king's mouth twitched. It started to turn up at the corners. Then he gave a beautifully big smile.

"I had forgotten about cartwheels and flying kites!" he said with glee. "I thought that they were a waste of time!"

"Silly Daddy!" said Princess Mia.

The king did a cartwheel and bounced onto his throne to pass some laws.

"From now on," said the king, "I decree that everyone must do at least ten cartwheels a day! We will teach silliness in schools! And everyone in the palace will have one hour off a day to practise kite flying!"

The king gave Princess Mia a beautiful charm necklace.

"This will remind you that everyone needs a little bit of silliness to keep them smiling," he said.

"Silly Daddy," said Princess Mia. "I've always known that!" And she danced out of the palace to play.

Hansel and Gretel

Hansel and Gretel lived by the forest with their father, a poor woodcutter, and their stepmother.

One evening, the family had nothing left to eat but a few crusts of bread. Hansel and Gretel went to bed hungry. As they lay in their beds, they heard the grown-ups talking.

"There are too many mouths to feed," said their stepmother. "We must take your children into the forest and leave them there."

"Never!" cried their father.

But the next morning, Hansel and Gretel's stepmother woke them early.

"Get up!" she ordered. "We're going into the forest to chop wood."

She handed them each a crust of bread for their lunch.

Hansel broke his bread into tiny pieces in his pocket, and as they walked, he secretly dropped a trail of crumbs on the ground.

Deep in the forest, Hansel and Gretel's father built them a fire.

"We are going to chop wood now," he said. "We'll return at sunset."

After a while, the children shared Gretel's bread, and then they curled up at the foot of an old oak tree and fell asleep.

When Hansel and Gretel woke up, they looked for the trail of breadcrumbs, but they were gone! The forest birds had eaten them.

"We'll wait till morning," Hansel said. "Then we can find our way home."

The next morning, the children walked through the forest, until they came to a little house – made of gingerbread! The roof was dripping with sugary icing, the door was made of candy canes and the garden was filled with colourful lollipops.

Delighted, the hungry children began to feast upon the sweets. As they ate, an old woman hobbled out of the house.

"You must be starving, my dears," she said. "Come inside and have a proper meal."

The old woman fed them well and then put them to bed. But Hansel and Gretel didn't know that the kind old woman was really a wicked witch. As she watched them sleep, she cackled, "I'll soon fatten these two up. Then they will make a proper meal for me!"

The following morning, the witch dragged Hansel from his bed, and threw him into a cage. Then she made Gretel cook her brother a big breakfast.

"Your brother is too skinny," the witch told Gretel. "I'll keep him locked up until he is nice and plump – and then I'll eat him up!"

Over the next few days, Hansel had as much food as he could eat. And every morning, the witch made him stick out his finger so she could feel whether he was fat enough to eat.

But Hansel knew that the old witch could hardly see, so he stuck a chicken bone through the cage instead.

"Still too scrawny," the witch would say.

One day the witch got tired of waiting and decided to eat Hansel right away.

"Light the oven!" the witch ordered Gretel. "Now crawl in and see if it's hot enough."

Gretel knew the witch was planning to cook her as well. So she decided to trick the witch.

"The oven's much too small for me," she said.

"Nincompoop!" cried the witch. "Even I could get into that oven. Look!" And she stuck her head inside.

With a great big shove, Gretel pushed the witch into the oven and slammed the door shut.

Gretel freed Hansel from his cage, and they danced happily around the kitchen. "We're safe! We're safe!" they sang. When the children looked around the witch's house, they found chests crammed with gold and sparkling jewels. They filled their pockets and set off for home.

They seemed to find their way straight home, where their delighted father greeted them with hugs and kisses.

He told them that their cruel stepmother had died, so they had nothing to fear. Hansel and Gretel showed him the treasure they had found.

"We will never go hungry again!" they said. They all lived happily ever after.

Index